Your Perfect Wedding Planner

C a t h y
B o u c h a r d

Designer of America's Largest Wedding Collection

CASABLANCA PRESS

A Divison of Sourcebooks, Inc.
Naperville, IL

Our Bridal Party

_____
Maid of Honor

_____
Matron of Honor

_____
Best Man

_____
Flower Girl

_____
Ring Bearer

Bridesmaids

Groomsmen

_____   _____

_____   _____

_____   _____

_____   _____

_____   _____

The
Wedding
of

&_____

on

_____

Published by Casablanca Press
A Division of Sourcebooks
P.O. Box 4410, Naperville, Illinois 60567 - 4410
(630) 961-3900
FAX: (630) 961-2168

Library of Congress Cataloging-in-Publication Data
Bouchard, Cathy.
    Your perfect wedding planner / Cathy Bouchard.
            p.   cm.
    ISBN 1-57071-168-2 (hc : alk. paper)
    1. Weddings—United States—Planning. 2. Wedding etiquette—United States. I. Title.
    HQ745.B73   1998
    395.2'2 — dc21
                                                                        97-6194
                                                                        CIP

Printed in the United States of America
UG 10 9 8 7 6 5 4

Dedication

Dedicated to my two most favorite brides—
daughters Jennifer and Melissa,
and to our favorite flower girl, their baby sister Kristin.

Introduction

Dear Bride-to-Be,

You're engaged! You're excited! You're overwhelmed! You are about to begin planning what will probably be the largest party you will ever host in your lifetime—or maybe you have opted for a simple, less elaborate event. Either way, thorough planning and attention to all those little details will be the key to a beautiful and perfect wedding.

I can't promise dream plans—planning a perfect wedding won't come stress-free. After all, there is much to do and never enough time to do it. But with this planner, I hope to save you hours of time and keep you informed, organized and efficient through this exciting process.

For your convenience, I have included over 100 worksheets, many of which are designed to double as vendor contracts, dozens of checklists, timelines and calendars, budget and expense forms, a personal phonebook, wedding directory, guest and gift lists, and much more for ease in planning your wedding. I have even included handy pockets for safe-keeping of all the receipts, fabric swatches and clippings you'll be referring to often, plus 'how-to' tips from wedding professionals.

With all this information to streamline your wedding planning, *Your Perfect Wedding Planner* will be your constant companion up until your wedding day. And when the rice has been thrown and the guests have gone home, it will become a treasured keepsake to bring back memories of this most wonderful time of your life.

Congratulations! May you have a perfect wedding!

All the Best,

Cathy J. Bouchard

Table of Contents

Table of Contents

Table of Contents

Table of Contents

Table of Contents

Table of Contents

Planning Your Wedding

Congratulations! You are engaged! This is an exciting time in your life—a time you have dreamed about for a very long time—your wedding!

This can also be a very stressful time, if you are not organized. This wedding planner enables you to stay organized and takes you step-by-step through all the preparations necessary for planning the perfect wedding. On your wedding day you can relax and enjoy all the excitement and attention surrounding you, assured that all the details are covered.

Wedding Planning Tips

Start by reviewing each section of this planner for an overview of what needs to be done. Each section pertains to a different element of planning your wedding. Included are many easy-to-use forms such as:

- A wedding timeline to know what needs to be done when.
- Checklists to ensure no detail is overlooked.
- Worksheets to use as agreement forms with wedding vendors.
- Forms to help you select and compare services of wedding vendors.
- Guest and gift lists.
- Budget and expense forms to help you estimate costs and stay within your budget.
- Monthly calendars to schedule appointments and keep notes.
- A wedding directory—your personal wedding phone book.

- Ceremony and reception supply lists.
- Bridal shopping lists.

The following important decisions need to be made before you start planning your wedding. After you have decided on the following, reserve your ceremony and reception sites; some locations could be booked up to a year in advance.

ESTIMATE THE SIZE OF YOUR GUEST LIST
This enables you to start searching for location sites and to estimate your budget.

SET A BUDGET
This will be determined by the size of your guest list, the number in your wedding party and the style of your wedding.

DECIDE ON YOUR WEDDING STYLE/THEME
Decide on your wedding theme or style and start searching for location sites. Keep in mind the time of year you want to have your wedding.

PICK A WEDDING DATE AND TIME
This may be determined by the availability of your ceremony and reception sites. Have two or three possible dates in mind.

As you are planning your wedding, it is important to stay organized, plan ahead and delegate duties.

STAY ORGANIZED
Remember to keep your planner with you at all times. You may have a moment to make a phone call or visit a bridal shop. When you talk or visit with wedding professionals, refer to the appropriate section in your wedding planner to know what questions to ask, record notes and important information and check your budget. Keep items you collect, such as brochures, price sheets and business cards, in the pockets provided in this planner.

PLAN AHEAD
Each task you complete will create more decisions for you to make. Thinking about how everything affects something else will help you plan ahead and ensure that everything runs smoothly on your wedding day. Ask yourself who, how, where and when, then plan how to take care of each circumstance. For instance, when you order your wedding cake, think about how it will get to the reception site, who will

get it there, when it should get there, where it will be set up (is there a decorated table for it?) and who will set it up. Then think about who will cut and serve the cake at the reception—do you have your special cake knife and serving set? How will the cake pillars get returned to the bakery while you are on your honeymoon?

DELEGATE DUTIES

Use the *List of Ceremony Helpers* (page 143) and the *List of Reception Helpers* (page 175) to help you delegate duties to responsible individuals. Each task that needs to be done should have someone assigned to it. Give copies of each form to your wedding day coordinators so they know who is responsible for what duty. On your wedding day, the only thing you will have to do is enjoy being the beautiful bride.

How to Use This Planner

Begin with the *Wedding Timeline* in this section. This master list gives you a time frame for completing each item and is separated into the different elements of your wedding: Pre-Wedding, The Ceremony, The Reception, The Honeymoon. At a glance you know what needs to be done when and for what event. Refer to the individual sections for more detailed information.

Start asking friends and family members for referrals on the services you need. Record the information in the *Wedding Vendors Referral Form* (pages 63–64). Watch your local newspaper for announcements of upcoming bridal shows. List the date, time and location on the *Bridal Show Calendar* (page 65). These shows are a great way to meet wedding professionals, see samples of their products and pick up information on their services.

As you set appointments and interview wedding professionals, complete the estimate forms provided in each section. Each form has a place to record the appointment date and time, the location of the business, your budget for that particular service and a list of important questions to ask them. This enables you to easily compare services and make the best hiring decision.

As you hire your wedding professionals, complete the worksheet that pertains to their service. These worksheets describe all details of products and services they will be providing and can be used as letters of agreement.

Complete *The Wedding Directory* pages as you select your bridal party and hire wedding professionals. Record the names, addresses and phone numbers of everyone involved in your wedding. This becomes your personal wedding phone book.

Write your appointments in the appropriate monthly calendars. Use the *Master Calendar* form to record important events so you can see them at a glance.

Working with Wedding Professionals

Part of organizing the many details that go into planning your wedding includes taking care of deposits and contracts. The most important things to remember when working with wedding professionals are:

ALWAYS ASK FOR REFERENCES
Get at least three references from each vendor, and follow up with each one.

GET ALL THE DETAILS IN WRITING
You should have a contract or letter of agreement with each wedding professional. Get everything in writing and sign a contract! The worksheets in this planner describe the details of products and services your wedding professionals provide, and can be used as letters of agreement.

PAY THE SMALLEST DEPOSIT YOU CAN AND PAY WITH CREDIT CARDS
Pay the smallest deposit you can and pay for everything with a credit card. Some credit card companies offer options that permit you to withhold payment for damaged or destroyed goods. You may also be able to dispute any charges for services not satisfactorily rendered. Check with your credit card company for any options and restrictions.

GET A RECEIPT
Get receipts for everything. It is easy to keep your receipts in one place by storing them in the pockets provided in this wedding planner.

CONFIRM DETAILS
Communication is very important. Confirm major details with each wedding vendor the month before the wedding and confirm all details two weeks before your wedding.

Wedding Timeline ———————————————

SIX TO TWELVE MONTHS BEFORE

☑ Announce your engagement.

☑ Check with newspapers regarding engagement announcements.

☑ Set the wedding budget and decide who pays for what.

☐ Decide on the wedding date and time.

☐ Decide on the style and color scheme of your wedding.

☑ Determine the size of your guest list.

☑ Start compiling the guest list.

☐ Choose your maid of honor and bridesmaids.

☐ Groom selects his best man and groomsmen.

☐ Start shopping for your wedding gown and bridesmaids' dresses.

☐ Select a photographer.

☐ Select a videographer.

☐ Select a florist.

☐ Reserve transportation.

The Ceremony

☐ Reserve the ceremony site.

☐ Choose officiant or clergymember.

☐ Start planning the ceremony.

☐ Hire organist/musicians and soloist/vocalist.

The Reception

☐ Reserve the reception site.

☐ Start planning the reception.

☐ Reserve caterer, if reception site doesn't provide catering.

☐ Reserve musicians/band/disc jockey.

The Honeymoon

☐ Start planning the honeymoon.

☐ Select a travel agent to help you with honeymoon arrangements.

☐ Obtain visas/passports for foreign honeymoon travel.

Planning Your Wedding

FOUR TO SIX MONTHS BEFORE
- ❑ Order bridal attire (if not already ordered).
- ❑ Purchase your bridal shoes, hosiery and accessories.
- ❑ Coordinate mothers' attire.
- ❑ Finalize the guest list and determine the number of invitations to order.
- ❑ Order the invitations and stationery.
- ❑ Design and print maps to be inserted in invitations.
- ❑ Start planning the rehearsal dinner (usually hosted by groom's family).
- ❑ Shop for wedding rings.
- ❑ Start shopping for wedding accessories.
- ❑ Register at specialty and department stores.
- ❑ Start making lodging and transportation arrangements for out-of-town attendants and guests.

The Ceremony
- ❑ Review or start writing your wedding vows.
- ❑ Decide on decorations.
- ❑ Hire or ask someone to be your ceremony coordinator.
- ❑ Start recruiting volunteers to help with duties.
- ❑ Determine items that need to be rented and make arrangements.

The Reception
- ❑ Hire or ask someone to be your reception coordinator.
- ❑ Start recruiting volunteers to help with duties.
- ❑ Decide on decorations.
- ❑ Determine items that need to be rented and make arrangements.
- ❑ Order the wedding cake.

The Honeymoon
- ❑ Continue planning the honeymoon.
- ❑ Purchase luggage.

Planning Your Wedding

TWO TO THREE MONTHS BEFORE

- ☐ Address invitations and announcements.
- ☐ Mail invitations (four to six weeks before the wedding).
- ☐ Plan bridesmaids' luncheon.
- ☐ Continue planning the rehearsal dinner.
- ☐ Shop for attendants' gifts.
- ☐ Shop for gifts for each other.
- ☐ Reserve men's formal wear.
- ☐ Schedule fittings for attire.
- ☐ Check with newspapers regarding wedding announcements.
- ☐ Have wedding portrait taken for newspaper announcement.
- ☐ Schedule beauty appointments.
- ☐ Continue making lodging and transportation arrangements for out-of-town attendants and guests.

The Ceremony

- ☐ Check marriage license requirements.
- ☐ Finalize ceremony details with officiant.
- ☐ Continue recruiting volunteers to help with duties.
- ☐ Fill in the *List of Ceremony Helpers* form.
- ☐ Make arrangements for the rehearsal.
- ☐ Make transportation arrangements for the bridal party to get to the ceremony.

The Reception

- ☐ Continue recruiting volunteers to help with duties.
- ☐ Fill in the *List of Reception Helpers* form.
- ☐ Purchase cake top decoration.
- ☐ Purchase cake knife and cake server, have engraved.
- ☐ Plan the menu.

The Honeymoon

- ☐ Finalize honeymoon plans.
- ☐ Reserve a romantic room for your wedding night.

Planning Your Wedding

ONE MONTH BEFORE

- ❑ Mail invitations (if not already done).
- ❑ Confirm major details of all wedding professionals and services.
- ❑ Pick up wedding rings, check sizes.
- ❑ Pick up wedding attire and make sure it fits.
- ❑ Make sure bridesmaids have their attire and accessories.
- ❑ Confirm men's formal wear order.
- ❑ Make sure you have all the accessories: ring pillow, toasting goblets, etc.
- ❑ Host bridesmaids' luncheon.
- ❑ Review attendant duties with the wedding party.
- ❑ Send thank-you notes for gifts already received.
- ❑ Try out your wedding day look with hair stylist and makeup artist.
- ❑ Give photographer a copy of the *Photo and Video Checklist*, showing which photos to take at the ceremony and reception.
- ❑ Give videographer a copy of the *Photo and Video Checklist*, showing which events to film at the ceremony and reception.
- ❑ Decide if you are having a receiving line; if so, decide who will participate and the order of the lineup. Also decide where to place it, at the ceremony or at the reception.
- ❑ Decide where to place the guest book—at the ceremony or at the reception.

The Ceremony

- ❑ Get marriage license.
- ❑ Finalize transportation arrangements for wedding party to get to ceremony site.
- ❑ Give musicians and vocalists a copy of *Ceremony Music Selections*.
- ❑ Fill in the *Ceremony Timetable* form.
- ❑ Finalize the ceremony rehearsal details.

The Reception

- ❑ Finalize transportation arrangements for wedding party to get to reception site.
- ❑ Give musicians/band/disc jockey a copy of *Reception Music Selections*.
- ❑ Fill in the *Reception Timetable* form.

The Honeymoon

- ❑ Start shopping and packing for your honeymoon.

Planning Your Wedding

One to Two Weeks Before

❑ Address and stamp wedding announcements.

❑ Give announcements to someone to mail out on or just after the day of the wedding.

❑ Final formal wear fittings.

❑ Confirm all details with wedding professionals.

❑ Pack your wedding day supplies, box together and label as to where they should be delivered: ceremony, dressing room, reception, etc.

❑ Remind the wedding party about the rehearsal and rehearsal dinner party.

❑ Send change-of-address cards, if necessary.

❑ Make arrangements to have your gown pressed prior to the ceremony.

❑ Continue sending thank-you notes for gifts already received.

❑ Reconfirm beauty appointments.

The Ceremony

❑ Review duties with ceremony volunteers/helpers.

❑ Attend the ceremony rehearsal and rehearsal dinner (the night before).

❑ Present gifts to attendants at the rehearsal dinner party (if not already done at the bridesmaids' luncheon and bachelor party).

❑ Prepare checks to give to officiant and musicians/vocalist.

❑ Make sure you have the marriage license.

❑ Fill in pew cards (if using them).

The Reception

❑ Review duties with reception volunteers/helpers.

❑ Give caterer final guest count.

❑ Go over seating arrangements with the caterer or site manager.

❑ Fill in *Reception Seating Chart* and write place cards (if you're having a large sit-down dinner).

The Honeymoon

❑ Confirm all honeymoon reservations.

❑ Confirm wedding night accommodations.

❑ Pick up tickets and traveler's checks.

❑ Finish shopping and packing.

Planning Your Wedding

YOUR WEDDING DAY
- ❑ Eat a good breakfast!
- ❑ Put your wedding gown, headpiece/veil, undergarments, accessories and other items you will need to get ready together in one place.
- ❑ Make sure the groom gives the best man your wedding band.
- ❑ Give the maid of honor the groom's wedding ring.
- ❑ Transfer your engagement ring to your right hand.
- ❑ Make sure you bring the marriage license.
- ❑ Have someone mail out the wedding announcements.

THREE HOURS BEFORE THE CEREMONY
- ❑ Hair and nails should be done.

TWO HOURS BEFORE THE CEREMONY
- ❑ Start getting dressed. If pictures are being taken before the ceremony, the wedding party should be dressed and ready two hours before the ceremony.

ONE HOUR BEFORE THE CEREMONY
- ❑ If photographs are being taken prior to the ceremony, the wedding party should arrive at least one hour before the ceremony and receive their flowers and boutonnieres. Be sure to arrange this with your florist.

THIRTY TO FORTY-FIVE MINUTES BEFORE THE CEREMONY
- ❑ The ushers should be ready to seat the guests. Guests should be seated as they arrive.

THIRTY MINUTES BEFORE THE CEREMONY
- ❑ The music should start twenty to thirty minutes before the ceremony begins.

FIVE MINUTES BEFORE THE CEREMONY
- ❑ The groom's parents should be seated five minutes before the ceremony begins.

IMMEDIATELY BEFORE THE CEREMONY
- ❑ The mother of the bride is seated immediately before the processional; then the aisle runner is rolled out, the groom and best man take their places; then the processional begins.

Groom's Timeline

AS SOON AS POSSIBLE

❑ Purchase the bride's engagement ring.
❑ With your fiancé: set the wedding budget and decide who pays for what.
❑ With your fiancé: set the wedding date.
❑ With your fiancé: choose the ceremony site.
❑ With your fiancé: select and meet with officiant to plan the ceremony.
❑ Write your wedding vows, or review vows with the officiant.
❑ Select your best man, groomsmen and ushers (one usher per every fifty guests).
❑ Start compiling your guest list.
❑ Start planning the honeymoon.
❑ Obtain visas/passports for foreign honeymoon travel.

FOUR TO SIX MONTHS BEFORE THE WEDDING

❑ Your guest list should be completed by now. Give list to bride.
❑ Buy wedding rings.
❑ With your parents and fiancé, begin planning the rehearsal dinner.
❑ Continue planning the honeymoon.

TWO TO THREE MONTHS BEFORE THE WEDDING

❑ Set date to get marriage license.
❑ Select the formal wear and reserve.
❑ Schedule formal wear fittings for you and your groomsmen.
❑ With your fiancé: meet with officiant to finalize the ceremony.
❑ Reserve wedding day transportation for the bridal party.
❑ Make lodging arrangements for out-of-town attendants and guests.
❑ Continue to assist your parents with the rehearsal dinner plans.
❑ Reserve wedding night accommodations.

ONE MONTH BEFORE THE WEDDING

❑ Pick up the wedding rings, make sure they fit.
❑ Have wedding bands engraved.
❑ Confirm that your groomsmen have been fitted for their formal wear.
❑ Purchase a gift for your bride.
❑ Finalize honeymoon plans.
❑ Purchase gifts for your groomsmen.

Planning Your Wedding

Two Weeks before the Wedding
- ❑ Schedule hair appointment.
- ❑ Final formal wear fittings.
- ❑ Attend bachelor party, present groomsmen with gifts.
- ❑ Reconfirm lodging arrangements for out-of-town guests.

One Week before the Wedding
- ❑ Pick up marriage license.
- ❑ Pick up and try on your formal wear.
- ❑ Confirm that your groomsmen pick up their formal wear.
- ❑ Reconfirm wedding day transportation.
- ❑ Give restaurant/caterer final guest count for rehearsal dinner party.
- ❑ Confirm date/time/locaton of the rehearsal and rehearsal dinner party with groomsmen.
- ❑ Reconfirm honeymoon plans.
- ❑ Begin packing for honeymoon.

Your Wedding Day
- ❑ Start getting ready at:
  Time_____ Location_____
- ❑ Give best man the bride's wedding ring.
- ❑ Give best man the officiant's fee in a sealed envelope (he needs to present it to the officiant after the ceremony and before the reception).
- ❑ Take marriage license to the ceremony.
- ❑ Arrive at the ceremony site at _____A.M./P.M.
- ❑ Wedding photographs will be taken _____

Wedding Day Checklist
- ❑ Marriage license
- ❑ Bride's wedding ring
- ❑ Officiant's fee
- ❑ Coat and trousers
- ❑ Shirt, tie, vest, cummerbund
- ❑ Socks and shoes
- ❑ Studs, cufflinks, suspenders
- ❑ Comb/brush
- ❑ Hairstyling spray
- ❑ Cologne
- ❑ Mints, mouth spray

Notes

_____

_____

_____

_____

_____

_____

_____

_____

_____

_____

_____

_____

_____

_____

_____

_____

_____

_____

_____

_____

_____

_____

_____

Master Calendar

hair & makeup   rehearsal dinner.
transportation
musician/band/DJ
honeymoon
registry

January	February
Dress	(table linen etc) food tasting & cake → march = not invited?
2nd reception	
photographer, Videographer?	
rings.	

• spot.
• mothers' attire
• 80% (mothers & ours)
• luxury

March	April
2nd deposit	
	men's wear
Registry.	
accessories invitations	@end = send out invitations.

May	June
Program	
seating chart & place cards	
Korea.	

* favors
* Addresses
  out of town guest info.

14

✯ Rehearsal dinner
✯ bridesmaids luncheon/dinner
✯ groomsmen   ''
✯ wedding party dinner/luncheon

Master Calendar

July	August
Honeymoon	Korea.

September	October

November	December

January _____ Months Before Wedding

Sun	Mon	Tues	Wed	Thurs	Fri	Sat

February _____ Months Before Wedding

Sun	Mon	Tues	Wed	Thurs	Fri	Sat

March _____ Months Before Wedding

Sun	Mon	Tues	Wed	Thurs	Fri	Sat

April _____ Months Before Wedding

Sun	Mon	Tues	Wed	Thurs	Fri	Sat

May _____ Months Before Wedding

Sun	Mon	Tues	Wed	Thurs	Fri	Sat

June _____ Months Before Wedding

Sun	Mon	Tues	Wed	Thurs	Fri	Sat

July _____ Months Before Wedding

Sun	Mon	Tues	Wed	Thurs	Fri	Sat

Planning Your Wedding

August _____ Months Before Wedding

Sun	Mon	Tues	Wed	Thurs	Fri	Sat

Planning Your Wedding

September _____ Months Before Wedding

Sun	Mon	Tues	Wed	Thurs	Fri	Sat

October _____ Months Before Wedding

Sun	Mon	Tues	Wed	Thurs	Fri	Sat

November _____ Months Before Wedding

Sun	Mon	Tues	Wed	Thurs	Fri	Sat

December ____ Months Before Wedding

Sun	Mon	Tues	Wed	Thurs	Fri	Sat
__	__	__	__	__	__	__
__	__	__	__	__	__	__
__	__	__	__	__	__	__
__	__	__	__	__	__	__
__	__	__	__	__	__	__

Wedding Week Itinerary

List parties, outings and events to be held the week before the wedding.

Monday	Tuesday

Wednesday	Thursday

Friday	Saturday/Sunday

The Day Before Schedule

6:00 A.M.

7:00 A.M.

8:00 A.M.

9:00 A.M.

10:00 A.M.

11:00 A.M.

12:00 P.M.

1:00 P.M.

2:00 P.M.

3:00 P.M.

4:00 P.M.

5:00 P.M.

6:00 P.M.

7:00 P.M.

8:00 P.M.

9:00 P.M.

10:00 P.M.

11:00 P.M.

Midnight

Wedding Day Schedule

6:00 A.M.

7:00 A.M.

8:00 A.M.

9:00 A.M.

10:00 A.M.

11:00 A.M.

12:00 P.M.

1:00 P.M.

2:00 P.M.

3:00 P.M.

4:00 P.M.

5:00 P.M.

6:00 P.M.

7:00 P.M.

8:00 P.M.

9:00 P.M.

10:00 P.M.

11:00 P.M.

Midnight

Wedding Day Supply Checklist

PERSONAL
- ☐ Anti-static cling spray
- ☐ Aspirin
- ☐ Bottled water and straws
- ☐ Breath mints
- ☐ Curlers or curling iron
- ☐ Deodorant
- ☐ Extra stockings
- ☐ Going-away outfit
- ☐ Hairbrush and comb
- ☐ Hairdryer
- ☐ Hairpins
- ☐ Hairspray
- ☐ Jewelry
- ☐ Kleenex
- ☐ Makeup kit
- ☐ Mirror
- ☐ Nail file
- ☐ Nail polish (clear and colored)
- ☐ Perfume
- ☐ Sewing kit and safety pins
- ☐ Spot remover
- ☐ Tampons and pads
- ☐ Toothbrush and toothpaste
- ☐ Towels
- ☐ Something old, new, borrowed and blue
- ☐ Wedding gown, veil, shoes, garter, slip and hosiery

GENERAL SUPPLIES
- ☐ This wedding planner
- ☐ Band-Aids/emergency kit
- ☐ Fan/heater
- ☐ Florist tape
- ☐ Glue
- ☐ Hammer and nails or tacks
- ☐ Iron and ironing board
- ☐ Scissors
- ☐ Straight pins
- ☐ String
- ☐ Tape: duct, scotch, masking
- ☐ Wire

THE CEREMONY
- ☐ Candles
- ☐ Decorations
- ☐ Flower girl's basket
- ☐ Guest register and pen
- ☐ Maps to the reception site
- ☐ Marriage license
- ☐ Officiant's fee in envelope
- ☐ Pew bows
- ☐ Rice, birdseed, flower petals, bubbles
- ☐ Ring bearer pillow
- ☐ Smelling salts (for fainting)
- ☐ Soloist fee in envelope
- ☐ Special vows/readings
- ☐ Wedding programs
- ☐ Wedding rings

THE RECEPTION
- ☐ Cake knife and server
- ☐ Cake top decoration
- ☐ Decorations
- ☐ Disposable cameras
- ☐ Guest mementos/party favors
- ☐ Guest register and pen
- ☐ Payments due
- ☐ Rice, birdseed, flower petals, bubbles
- ☐ Table centerpieces
- ☐ Toasting goblets

The Wedding Budget

Budget Planning Tips

Setting a budget is the first step you need to take in planning your wedding. Your budget will be determined by the style of your wedding, number of guests and the type of reception you have. Everything you do will affect your wedding budget. The costs will go up for each attendant added to the bridal party as well as each addition to the guest list.

It is important to keep accurate financial records as you plan your wedding.

The wedding budget in this section is divided into fifteen categories. There are columns for writing in what you estimate an item to cost, what the actual cost is and who is responsible for paying for it. At the end of each category is a subtotal column. You can transfer these subtotal amounts to the *Budget Overview*. This will give you your total wedding budget. Keeping a record of the actual expenses as you go along will help you stay within your budget.

Keep this wedding planner with you to record important information as you are shopping, making phone calls and meeting with wedding professionals.

How to Determine Your Budget

To determine your budget you can allocate a certain percentage to each aspect of the wedding. You should have a separate budget for the honeymoon. The reception

will typically account for 40% of your budget. The remaining 60% can be allocated according to your priorities. Following is a sample of one possible way to divide it up:

40% reception, 15% photography and video, 10% wedding attire, 10% flowers and decorations, 5% ceremony, 5% music, 4% invitations and stationery, 4% miscellaneous, 3% rentals, 2% wedding cake, 2% transportation.

Hidden Costs

Unbudgeted costs can result in unexpected higher wedding bills. Being aware of "details" will help you avoid any hidden costs. The worksheets throughout the planner and the comprehensive budget in this section should provide you with a list of all the expenses that can be incurred. Things to keep in mind are: taxes and gratuities, corkage fees, a fee to cut and serve your cake, extra fees for china and flatware not included in the catering bill, extra fees for table and chair rentals, parking fees, coat check fees, cost to have your gown cleaned and preserved, cost to preserve your bridal bouquet, an extra bridal bouquet to toss, etc.

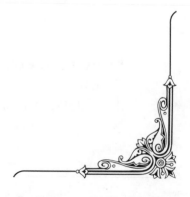

The Wedding Budget

Who Pays for What

Today there are no rules about who pays for what. The following is a list of wedding expenses and how they are traditionally divided, if you wish to follow these guidelines. Times have changed and what it really comes down to is the financial ability of the bride and groom and their families. You should all get together to discuss the type of wedding you want to have and set a realistic budget. Use the following worksheet to help you determine who will be responsible for which expenses so there are no misunderstandings.

Person Responsible

THE BRIDE

1. Groom's wedding ring _____

2. Gift for the groom _____

3. Gifts for bridesmaids _____

4. Personal stationery _____

5. Physical exam/blood test _____

THE BRIDE'S FAMILY

1. Bride's wedding attire _____

2. Bridal consultant's fee _____

3. Engagement party _____

4. Engagement portrait _____

5. Wedding portrait _____

6. Bridesmaids' luncheon _____

7. Invitations and announcements _____

8. Postage for invitations _____

9. Gift for the newlyweds _____

The Ceremony

10. Site rental fee _____

11. Bridesmaids' bouquets

The Wedding Budget

Person Responsible

12. Decorations and rentals _____

13. Music: organist, soloists _____

14. Photography _____

15. Videography _____

16. Transportation for bridal party _____
    to ceremony and reception

The Reception

17. Site rental fee _____

18. Decorations and flowers _____

19. Catering _____

20. Beverages _____

21. Music and entertainment _____

22. Wedding cake _____

23. Accessories _____

24. Gratuities for bartenders _____
    and waiters

25. Parking costs _____

26. Coat check fees _____

THE GROOM

1. Bride's engagement and _____
   wedding rings

2. Gift for the bride _____

3. Gifts to groomsmen _____

4. Bride's going-away corsage _____

5. Rehearsal dinner _____

6. Physical exam/blood test _____

The Wedding Budget

Person Responsible

The Ceremony

7. Marriage license ⎯⎯⎯⎯⎯⎯⎯⎯⎯⎯⎯⎯⎯⎯

8. Officiant's fee ⎯⎯⎯⎯⎯⎯⎯⎯⎯⎯⎯⎯⎯⎯

9. Bride's bouquet ⎯⎯⎯⎯⎯⎯⎯⎯⎯⎯⎯⎯⎯⎯

10. Boutonnieres for men in
    wedding party ⎯⎯⎯⎯⎯⎯⎯⎯⎯⎯⎯⎯⎯⎯

11. Mothers' corsages ⎯⎯⎯⎯⎯⎯⎯⎯⎯⎯⎯⎯⎯⎯

12. His formal wear and accessories ⎯⎯⎯⎯⎯⎯⎯⎯⎯⎯⎯⎯⎯⎯

The Honeymoon

13. All honeymoon expenses ⎯⎯⎯⎯⎯⎯⎯⎯⎯⎯⎯⎯⎯⎯

Family Members

- Rehearsal dinner (groom's family)
- Clothes for the wedding
- Lodging and travel expenses
- Wedding gift for bride and groom

The Attendants

- Bridal shower (maid of honor and bridesmaids)
- Bachelor party (best man and groomsmen)
- Wedding attire
- Lodging and travel expenses
- Wedding gift for bride and groom

The Wedding Budget

Wedding Expenses ——————————————————————————

	Estimate	Actual	Paid By
WEDDING RINGS			
Engagement ring	_____	_____	_____
Bride's wedding ring	_____	_____	_____
Groom's wedding ring	_____	_____	_____
Subtotal	$_____	$_____	
BRIDAL CONSULTANT	$_____	$_____	_____
PRE-WEDDING ACTIVITIES			
Engagement party	_____	_____	_____
Bridesmaids' luncheon	_____	_____	_____
Rehearsal dinner	_____	_____	_____
Other	_____	_____	_____
Subtotal	$_____	$_____	
WEDDING ATTIRE			
Bride's wedding gown	_____	_____	_____
Veil and headpiece	_____	_____	_____
Slip	_____	_____	_____
Shoes	_____	_____	_____
Stockings	_____	_____	_____
Garter	_____	_____	_____
Gloves	_____	_____	_____
Jewelry	_____	_____	_____
Alterations	_____	_____	_____
Gown pressing	_____	_____	_____
Dry cleaning	_____	_____	_____
Gown preserving	_____	_____	_____
Groom's formal wear	_____	_____	_____
Groom's accessories	_____	_____	_____
Bridesmaids' attire	_____	_____	_____
Ushers' attire	_____	_____	_____
Other	_____	_____	_____
Subtotal	$_____	$_____	

The Wedding Budget

	Estimate	Actual	Paid By
BEAUTY			
Hair			
Makeup			
Manicure			
Pedicure			
Facial			
Massage			
Other			
Subtotal	$	$	
THE CEREMONY			
Site fee			
Officiant's fee			
Marriage license			
Musicians			
Vocalist			
Decorations			
Rentals			
Unity candle			
Guest register			
Pen with penholder			
Ring bearer pillow			
Flower girl basket			
Other			
Subtotal	$	$	
THE RECEPTION			
Site fee			
Caterer/food			
Gratuity			
Liquor			
Corkage fee			
Beverages			

The Wedding Budget

	Estimate	Actual	Paid By
Wedding cake			
Cake delivery fee			
Cake setup fee			
Cake top decoration			
Cake knife and server			
Groom's cake			
Music/entertainment			
Decorations			
Balloons			
Tent/canopy			
Dance floor			
Tables			
Chairs			
Linens			
Tableware			
Toasting glasses			
Table centerpieces			
Party favors			
Disposable cameras			
Heaters/fans			
Parking fee			
Valet service			
Rice, seeds, bubbles			
Flower petals to toss			
Other			
Subtotal	$	$	

RENTALS

	Estimate	Actual	Paid By
Table centerpieces			
Mail card box			
Decorative pillars			
Decorative columns			
Statuaries			

The Wedding Budget

	Estimate	Actual	Paid By
Other	_____	_____	_____
Subtotal	$ _____	$ _____	

STATIONERY

	Estimate	Actual	Paid By
Invitations	_____	_____	_____
Response cards	_____	_____	_____
Reception cards	_____	_____	_____
Pew cards	_____	_____	_____
Church cards	_____	_____	_____
Rain cards	_____	_____	_____
Maps	_____	_____	_____
Wedding programs	_____	_____	_____
Place cards	_____	_____	_____
Announcements	_____	_____	_____
Thank-you notes	_____	_____	_____
Personal stationery	_____	_____	_____
Stamps	_____	_____	_____
Calligraphy	_____	_____	_____
Other	_____	_____	_____
Subtotal	$ _____	$ _____	

FLOWERS

	Estimate	Actual	Paid By
Ceremony site	_____	_____	_____
Reception site	_____	_____	_____
Bride's bouquet	_____	_____	_____
Silk toss bouquet	_____	_____	_____
Maid of honor's flowers	_____	_____	_____
Bridesmaids' flowers	_____	_____	_____
Flower girl basket	_____	_____	_____
Boutonnieres	_____	_____	_____
Corsages	_____	_____	_____
Other	_____	_____	_____
Subtotal	$ _____	$ _____	

The Wedding Budget

	Estimate	Actual	Paid By
PHOTOGRAPHY			
Formal portraits			
Wedding album			
Parents' albums			
Extra prints			
Other			
Subtotal	$	$	
VIDEOGRAPHY			
Main video			
Extra copies			
Other			
Subtotal	$	$	
TRANSPORTATION			
Limousine			
Car rentals			
Other			
Subtotal	$	$	
GIFTS			
Honor attendant(s)			
Best man			
Bridesmaids			
Groomsmen			
Bride's gift			
Groom's gift			
Other			
Subtotal	$	$	

The Wedding Budget

	Estimate	Actual	Paid By
OTHER ACCESSORIES			
Wedding day "emergency kit"	_____	_____	_____
Money envelope bag	_____	_____	_____
Bride's tote bag	_____	_____	_____
Bridal pouch	_____	_____	_____
Ring bearer chest	_____	_____	_____
Ring box	_____	_____	_____
Heart-shaped box	_____	_____	_____
Lucky sixpence	_____	_____	_____
Lucky penny	_____	_____	_____
Keepsake or video box	_____	_____	_____
Other	_____	_____	_____
Subtotal	$ _____	$ _____	
HONEYMOON			
Wedding night hotel	_____	_____	_____
Wardrobe	_____	_____	_____
Luggage	_____	_____	_____
Travel	_____	_____	_____
Transportation	_____	_____	_____
Accommodations	_____	_____	_____
Meals	_____	_____	_____
Spending money	_____	_____	_____
Other	_____	_____	_____
Subtotal	$ _____	$ _____	

The Wedding Budget

Budget Overview

	Estimate	Actual	Paid By
Wedding rings	_____	_____	_____
Bridal consultant	_____	_____	_____
Pre-wedding activities	_____	_____	_____
Wedding attire	_____	_____	_____
Beauty	_____	_____	_____
The ceremony	_____	_____	_____
The reception	_____	_____	_____
Rentals	_____	_____	_____
Stationery	_____	_____	_____
Flowers	_____	_____	_____
Photography	_____	_____	_____
Videography	_____	_____	_____
Transportation	_____	_____	_____
Gifts	_____	_____	_____
Other accessories	_____	_____	_____
Honeymoon	_____	_____	_____
Other Items:			
_____	_____	_____	_____
_____	_____	_____	_____
_____	_____	_____	_____
_____	_____	_____	_____
Total Budget	$ _____	$ _____	

The Wedding Directory

*B*ride's Attendants

MAID OF HONOR _____
Address _____
Phone: Home _____ Work _____ Fax/Email_____

BRIDESMAID_____
Address _____
Phone: Home _____ Work _____ Fax/Email_____

BRIDESMAID_____
Address _____
Phone: Home _____ Work _____ Fax/Email_____

BRIDESMAID_____
Address _____
Phone: Home _____ Work _____ Fax/Email_____

BRIDESMAID_____
Address _____
Phone: Home _____ Work _____ Fax/Email_____

The Wedding Directory

BRIDESMAID_____
Address _____
Phone: Home _____ Work _____ Fax/Email_____

BRIDESMAID_____
Address _____
Phone: Home _____ Work _____ Fax/Email_____

BRIDESMAID_____
Address _____
Phone: Home _____ Work _____ Fax/Email_____

BRIDESMAID_____
Address _____
Phone: Home _____ Work _____ Fax/Email_____

FLOWER GIRL _____
Address _____
Phone: Home _____ Work _____ Fax/Email_____

Groom's Attendants

BEST MAN_____
Address _____
Phone: Home _____ Work _____ Fax/Email_____

GROOMSMAN/USHER_____
Address _____
Phone: Home _____ Work _____ Fax/Email_____

GROOMSMAN/USHER_____
Address _____
Phone: Home _____ Work _____ Fax/Email_____

GROOMSMAN/USHER_____
Address _____
Phone: Home _____ Work _____ Fax/Email_____

The Wedding Directory

GROOMSMAN/USHER _____
Address _____
Phone: Home _____ Work _____ Fax/Email_____

GROOMSMAN/USHER _____
Address _____
Phone: Home _____ Work _____ Fax/Email_____

GROOMSMAN/USHER _____
Address _____
Phone: Home _____ Work _____ Fax/Email_____

GROOMSMAN/USHER _____
Address _____
Phone: Home _____ Work _____ Fax/Email_____

GROOMSMAN/USHER _____
Address _____
Phone: Home _____ Work _____ Fax/Email_____

RING BEARER _____
Address _____
Phone: Home _____ Work _____ Fax/Email_____

Family Members

BRIDE _____
Address _____
Phone: Home _____ Work _____ Fax/Email_____

GROOM _____
Address _____
Phone: Home _____ Work _____ Fax/Email_____

BRIDE'S MOTHER _____
Address _____
Phone: Home _____ Work _____ Fax/Email_____

The Wedding Directory

BRIDE'S FATHER _____
Address _____
Phone: Home _____ Work _____ Fax/Email_____

GROOM'S MOTHER_____
Address _____
Phone: Home _____ Work _____ Fax/Email_____

GROOM'S FATHER _____
Address _____
Phone: Home _____ Work _____ Fax/Email_____

NAME _____
Address _____
Phone: Home _____ Work _____ Fax/Email_____

NAME _____
Address _____
Phone: Home _____ Work _____ Fax/Email_____

NAME _____
Address _____
Phone: Home _____ Work _____ Fax/Email_____

NAME _____
Address _____
Phone: Home _____ Work _____ Fax/Email_____

Ceremony Services

CEREMONY SITE MANAGER _____
Address _____
Phone: Home _____ Work _____ Fax/Email_____

OFFICIANT/CLERGYMEMBER _____
Address _____
Phone: Home _____ Work _____ Fax/Email_____

The Wedding Directory

SOLOIST_____
Address _____
Phone: Home _____ Work _____ Fax/Email_____

ORGANIST _____
Address _____
Phone: Home _____ Work _____ Fax/Email_____

MUSICIAN _____
Address _____
Phone: Home _____ Work _____ Fax/Email_____

PHOTOGRAPHER _____
Address _____
Phone: Home _____ Work _____ Fax/Email_____

VIDEOGRAPHER _____
Address _____
Phone: Home _____ Work _____ Fax/Email_____

FLORIST/DECORATIONS _____
Address _____
Phone: Home _____ Work _____ Fax/Email_____

TRANSPORTATION _____
Address _____
Phone: Home _____ Work _____ Fax/Email_____

RENTALS _____
Address _____
Phone: Home _____ Work _____ Fax/Email_____

Reception Services

RECEPTION SITE MANAGER _____
Address _____
Phone: Home _____ Work _____ Fax/Email_____

The Wedding Directory

CATERER _____
Address _____
Phone: Home _____ Work _____ Fax/Email_____

BAKERY _____
Address _____
Phone: Home _____ Work _____ Fax/Email_____

FLORIST/DECORATIONS _____
Address _____
Phone: Home _____ Work _____ Fax/Email_____

MUSICIANS/DJ _____
Address _____
Phone: Home _____ Work _____ Fax/Email_____

RENTALS _____
Address _____
Phone: Home _____ Work _____ Fax/Email_____

GUEST REGISTER ATTENDANT _____
Address _____
Phone: Home _____ Work _____ Fax/Email_____

GIFT ATTENDANT _____
Address _____
Phone: Home _____ Work _____ Fax/Email_____

SERVICE _____
Address _____
Phone: Home _____ Work _____ Fax/Email_____

SERVICE _____
Address _____
Phone: Home _____ Work _____ Fax/Email_____

Wedding Professionals

WEDDING COORDINATOR _____

Address _____

Phone: Home _____ Work _____ Fax/Email_____

BRIDAL SALON _____

Address _____

Phone: Home _____ Work _____ Fax/Email_____

FORMAL WEAR STORE _____

Address _____

Phone: Home _____ Work _____ Fax/Email_____

JEWELER _____

Address _____

Phone: Home _____ Work _____ Fax/Email_____

STATIONER _____

Address _____

Phone: Home _____ Work _____ Fax/Email_____

TRANSPORTATION _____

Address _____

Phone: Home _____ Work _____ Fax/Email_____

REHEARSAL DINNER _____

Address _____

Phone: Home _____ Work _____ Fax/Email_____

WEDDING NIGHT ACCOMODATIONS _____

Address _____

Phone: Home _____ Work _____ Fax/Email_____

TRAVEL AGENCY _____

Address _____

Phone: Home _____ Work _____ Fax/Email_____

The Wedding Directory

SERVICE_____
Address _____
Phone: Home _____ Work _____ Fax/Email_____

SERVICE_____
Address _____
Phone: Home _____ Work _____ Fax/Email_____

SERVICE_____
Address _____
Phone: Home _____ Work _____ Fax/Email_____

SERVICE_____
Address _____
Phone: Home _____ Work _____ Fax/Email_____

SERVICE_____
Address _____
Phone: Home _____ Work _____ Fax/Email_____

SERVICE_____
Address _____
Phone: Home _____ Work _____ Fax/Email_____

SERVICE_____
Address _____
Phone: Home _____ Work _____ Fax/Email_____

SERVICE_____
Address _____
Phone: Home _____ Work _____ Fax/Email_____

SERVICE_____
Address _____
Phone: Home _____ Work _____ Fax/Email_____

Please make duplicate copies if necessary

Pre-Wedding Activities

Shopping for Your Engagement and Wedding Rings

Your engagement ring is a symbol of your love that will last forever and is, of course, priceless. But you do have to be practical. Start by setting a realistic budget, then shop around and choose a reputable jeweler. Look for stores that display the American Gem Society (AGS) logo. The AGS is an association of fine jewelers dedicated to consumer protection. Every member jeweler subscribes to a rigorous set of ethical and professional standards and is tested and recertified annually. When purchasing a diamond from your AGS jeweler, request an AGS Laboratory "Diamond Quality Document." Also, make sure the jeweler or salesperson you are working with is a certified gemologist with the Gemological Institute of America (GIA).

Contact the AGS for the name of your nearest American Gem Society jeweler and to receive a consumer information kit: American Gem Society, 8881 W. Sahara Ave., Las Vegas, Nevada 89117, 800-346-8485.

Selecting Your Engagement and Wedding Rings

ENGAGEMENT RINGS
There are many styles of rings to choose from. You'll want to try on a variety of rings to help determine what appeals to you in terms of the shape and setting. While the diamond is the most popular engagement ring choice, some brides prefer

colored stones, semiprecious stones or their birthstone. You can also combine the engagement and wedding ring by having a wider wedding band that is set with a solitaire.

TRADITIONAL BIRTHSTONES
January - Garnet
February - Amethyst
March - Aquamarine
April - Diamond
May - Emerald
June - Pearl
July - Ruby
August - Peridot
September - Sapphire
October - Opal
November - Topaz
December - Turquoise

SELECTING THE SHAPE FOR A DIAMOND ENGAGEMENT RING
You will be wearing your engagement and wedding rings every day, so when you select the shape of the stone, consider your lifestyle. A diamond is very hard but it can still chip or break. If you are very active, a ring with pointed edges, such as the marquise, is more vulnerable to breaking or chipping. There are seven basic diamond shapes. The round brilliant is the most popular shape.

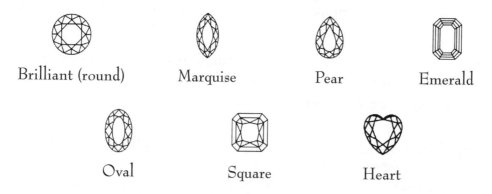

Brilliant (round)   Marquise   Pear   Emerald

Oval   Square   Heart

WEDDING RINGS

Gold - The gold wedding ring is very popular and is usually yellow or white in color. Wedding bands can be studded with diamonds or colored stones that go partially or all the way around the ring. Be sure to look for the quality or karat mark, 14K or 18K, imprinted on the inside of the ring.

Platinum - This rare metal is growing in popularity for couples looking for something different. Platinum is the strongest precious jewelry metal and costs more than gold—but it will last a lifetime and won't tarnish or wear out. Platinum can also be combined with 18 karat gold in both wedding and engagement rings, creating a very dramatic effect.

Buying a Quality Stone: The 4C's

The quality of a diamond has nothing to do with size or color alone. Subtle differences in quality can greatly affect the value and price. Understanding the 4C's will help you select a diamond of the best quality and value.

Cut: Many people confuse the cut with the shape of a diamond. The cut is the most important of the 4C's, because a well-cut diamond is better able to handle light, creating more sparkle.

Color: The best color for a diamond is no color. A totally colorless diamond best allows the stone to reflect light. Diamonds are rated for color on a scale from D, which is the highest rating (colorless), to Z, the lowest color rating.

Clarity: Most diamonds contain very tiny inclusions, or flaws, visible only through a jeweler's loupe. The fewer and smaller the inclusions are, the less they will interfere with the passage of light through the diamond. Most jewelers use the following rating system that will help you understand the clarity of your stone. Flawless stones are very rare, and are the most valuable and expensive.

FL (flawless)

IF (internally flawless—minor surface blemishes)

VVS1 - VVS2 (very, very small inclusions)

VS1 - VS2 (very small inclusions)

SI1 - SI2 (small inclusions)

I_1 - I_2 - I_3 (Imperfect—eye-visible inclusions)

Carat: The weight of the diamond is measured in carats. One carat is divided into 100 points. So a diamond of 50 points weighs .50 carat, or 1/2 of a carat. Two

diamonds of equal weight can have very unequal value, depending on their other characteristics. Fine quality can be found in diamonds of all shapes and sizes.

Caring for Your Wedding Rings

Your engagement and wedding rings will get soiled and smudged from normal wear and tear. You should apply lotions, soaps, hairspray and perfume before you put on your rings. Remove your rings before doing any rough work and avoid direct contact with chlorine bleach or chlorinated pool water, as it can discolor the mounting.

Your rings should be cleaned regularly to keep them looking beautiful. You can clean your rings in a commercial jewelry cleaner or in your own solution. Soak your rings in a solution of half cold water and half household ammonia for thirty minutes. Lift out, rinse and drain on a soft cloth or tissue paper.

Take your rings to your jeweler every year to have them professionally cleaned and to make sure the settings are secure.

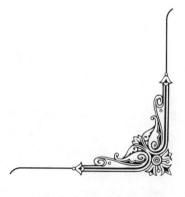

Wedding Rings Checklist

Due Date	To Do

❑ _____ Set a budget for the rings.

❑ _____ Purchase bride's engagement ring.

❑ _____ Purchase bride's wedding band.

❑ _____ Purchase groom's wedding band.

❑ _____ Have rings sized. Be sure to find out if there is an extra charge for sizing the rings.

❑ _____ Have wedding bands engraved. Be sure to allow enough time to have the rings back before your wedding. Wedding bands are usually engraved with the initials of the bride and groom and the wedding date.

Bride's wedding band wording:

example: *To C.J.B. from M.J.L. 5-1-98*

_____

Groom's wedding band wording:

example: *To M.A.B. from T.J.G. 2-28-98*

_____

❑ _____ Have your stone graded. Get a certificate with proof of your diamond's identity and grade. Be sure your stone is graded **out** of the setting. Ask about any fees for the report, and how long it will take so you can have the ring back in time for your wedding.

❑ _____ Have rings appraised. The store where you purchased your ring can appraise it, but it's better to have an independent appraiser look at the stone. Be sure to tell the appraiser that you're having it appraised for insurance purposes.

The written appraisal should include the following:
- A thorough description or photograph of the item
- The 4C's: cut, color, clarity and carat weight of the stone
- The estimated replacement value of the item

Due Date	To Do
❏ _____	Have rings insured. List the diamond on your Personal Articles Policy to insure it if it gets chipped, broken, lost or misplaced. Your homeowners policy will only protect it against theft or fire. Your insurance company will probably need the purchase agreement from your jeweler and/or an appraisal with a complete description of the item. Have your rings appraised every few years and update your insurance policy with the current replacement value of your rings.
❏ _____	Put a copy of the appraisal along with a photograph of your rings in a safe deposit box.
❏ _____	Keep the wedding rings in a safe place until the day of your wedding.

HELPFUL TIPS

On the day of the wedding, just prior to the ceremony, remember to give the bride's wedding band to the best man, and give the groom's wedding band to the maid of honor.

While you are dressing for your wedding, remember to switch your engagement ring to your right hand. During the ceremony, after the wedding ring has been placed on your finger, return your engagement ring to that finger.

If you will be wearing gloves, they must be removed before the ring is placed on your finger. If you are wearing long gloves, you might consider opening the seam of the ring finger of the left hand glove.

Wedding Rings Shopping Worksheet ————————

Use this form to help you decide what type of ring you want and to shop around and compare styles and prices. Once you know the rating and weight of a stone, you can compare similar stones for the best quality and value.

Bride's ring size _____

Groom's ring size _____

SHAPE PREFERENCE:

❑ Brilliant ❑ Marquise ❑ Pear ❑ Emerald

❑ Oval ❑ Square ❑ Heart

STYLE PREFERENCE:

❑ Traditional set ❑ Heirloom jewel

❑ Custom-designed ❑ Solitaire

SETTING PREFERENCE:

❑ 14K ❑ 18K ❑ Yellow gold ❑ White gold ❑ Platinum

ESTIMATES:

Store _____

Phone _____ Contact _____

Cost _____

Shape _____ Setting _____

Carat weight _____ Clarity rating _____

Color rating _____

Description _____

Comments _____

Please make duplicate copies if necessary

Wedding Rings Worksheet —————————————————

Jewelry Store _____

Address _____

Phone _____ Contact_____

Financing available _____

Guarantees / Warranties _____

Exchange policy _____

Return policy_____

BRIDE'S ENGAGEMENT RING DESCRIPTION

Date purchased _____ Date to pick up ring_____

Cost $_____ Sizing fee $_____

Appraisal fee $ _____

Budget $_____ Actual $_____

Paid by: ❑ Credit Card ❑ Check ❑ Cash

Deposit _____ Date due _____ ❑ Deposit paid

Balance _____ Date due _____ ❑ Balance paid

Ring size _____

Shape:	❑ Brilliant	❑ Marquise	❑ Pear	❑ Heart
	❑ Emerald	❑ Oval	❑ Square	
Setting:	❑ 14K	❑ 18K	❑ Yellow gold	
	❑ White gold	❑ Platinum		

Color rating _____ Clarity rating _____ Carat-weight_____

Description _____

_____

INSURANCE INFORMATION

Insurance Company_____

Address_____

Phone _____ Contact_____

Policy Number _____

SAFETY DEPOSIT BOX INFORMATION

Bank_____

Address_____

Phone _____ Contact_____

Account/Box number_____

❑ Copy of appraisal in safety deposit box

❑ Photograph of rings in safety deposit box

Pre-Wedding Activities

BRIDE'S WEDDING RING DESCRIPTION

Date purchased _____   Date to pick up ring_____

Cost $_____   Sizing fee $ _____

Appraisal fee $ _____

Budget $ _____   Actual $ _____

Paid by: ❏ Credit Card   ❏ Check   ❏ Cash

Deposit _____   Date due _____   ❏ Deposit paid

Balance _____   Date due _____   ❏ Balance paid

Ring size _____

Description _____

_____

_____

Engraving _____

_____

GROOM'S WEDDING RING DESCRIPTION

Date purchased _____   Date to pick up ring_____

Cost $_____   Sizing fee $ _____

Appraisal fee $ _____

Budget $ _____   Actual $ _____

Paid by: ❏ Credit Card   ❏ Check   ❏ Cash

Deposit _____   Date due _____   ❏ Deposit paid

Balance _____   Date due _____   ❏ Balance paid

Ring size _____

Description _____

_____

_____

Engraving _____

_____

Newspaper Announcements ————————————

ANNOUNCING YOUR ENGAGEMENT

An engagement announcement usually appears two to three months before the date of the wedding. An announcement can appear in the local newspaper in both of your hometowns. Call the newspapers where you want to announce your engagement and ask for the following information:

Publication _____

Mailing address _____

City _____ State _____ Zip_____

Phone ( ) _____ Contact_____

Does the newspaper provide a form? ❏ Yes ❏ No

Deadline for submission_____

Date to appear_____

Will they accept a photo? ❏ Yes ❏ No

    If yes, what format? (color, b & w, glossy) _____

    What size? _____

If you do submit a photo, print your name and phone number on the back in case it gets misplaced or separated from your announcement.

Will they return the photo? ❏ Yes ❏ No

Be sure to include a stamped, padded return envelope and to print your name, address and "please return" on the back of the photo.

Sample Engagement Wording:

Mr. and Mrs. (bride's parents' names) of (city, state) announce the engagement of their daughter, (your first and middle names), to Mr. (your fiancé's first and last names), the son of Mr. and Mrs. (your fiancé's parents' names) of (fiancé's parents' city, state). A (month of wedding) wedding is planned.

Pre-Wedding Activities

ANNOUNCING YOUR WEDDING

A wedding announcement can appear in the local newspaper in both of your hometowns. Call the newspapers where you want to announce your wedding and ask for the following information:

Publication _____

Mailing address _____

City _____ State _____ Zip _____

Phone ( ) _____ Contact_____

Does the newspaper provide a form?   ❑ Yes ❑ No

Deadline for submission_____

Date to appear _____

Will they accept a photo?   ❑ Yes ❑ No

    If yes, what format? (color, b & w, glossy) _____

    What size? _____

If you do submit a photo, print your name and phone number on the back in case it gets misplaced or separated from your announcement.

Will they return the photo?   ❑ Yes ❑ No

Be sure to include a stamped, padded return envelope and to print your name, address and "please return" on the back of the photo.

The following information could be included in your wedding announcement:
* Bride's full maiden name, or name after the wedding
* Groom's full name
* Current occupations
* Schools, military service and social organizations of bride and groom
* Bride's parents' names
* Groom's parents' names
* Wedding location
* Wedding date
* Description of wedding attire
* Officiant's name

Pre-Wedding Activities

- Names of family members in the wedding
- Names of those in the wedding party
- Reception location
- Information about special guests
- Honeymoon plans
- Location where you will reside

ENGAGEMENT ANNOUNCEMENT WORDING:

_____
_____
_____
_____
_____
_____
_____
_____
_____
_____

WEDDING ANNOUNCEMENT WORDING:

_____
_____
_____
_____
_____
_____
_____
_____
_____
_____
_____

Wedding Vendors Referral Form ———————

Contact local bridal publications and associations for referrals to wedding professionals in your area.

Bridal association _____ Phone ( ) _____

Bridal publication _____ Phone ( ) _____

SERVICE	WEDDING PROFESSIONAL	PHONE
Bridal Consultants:	_____	( ) _____
	_____	( ) _____
	_____	( ) _____
Bridal Salons:	_____	( ) _____
	_____	( ) _____
	_____	( ) _____
Formal Wear Stores:	_____	( ) _____
	_____	( ) _____
	_____	( ) _____
Rehearsal Dinner Locations:	_____	( ) _____
	_____	( ) _____
	_____	( ) _____
Ceremony Sites:	_____	( ) _____
	_____	( ) _____
	_____	( ) _____
Reception Sites:	_____	( ) _____
	_____	( ) _____
	_____	( ) _____
Caterers:	_____	( ) _____
	_____	( ) _____
	_____	( ) _____

Pre-Wedding Activities

Service	Wedding Professional	Phone
Wedding Cakes/ Bakery:	_____	( ) _____
	_____	( ) _____
	_____	( ) _____
Florists:	_____	( ) _____
	_____	( ) _____
	_____	( ) _____
Rentals/ Party Stores:	_____	( ) _____
	_____	( ) _____
	_____	( ) _____
Photographers:	_____	( ) _____
	_____	( ) _____
	_____	( ) _____
Videographers:	_____	( ) _____
	_____	( ) _____
	_____	( ) _____
Musicians/ DJ's:	_____	( ) _____
	_____	( ) _____
	_____	( ) _____
Limousine Services:	_____	( ) _____
	_____	( ) _____
	_____	( ) _____
Travel Agency:	_____	( ) _____
	_____	( ) _____
	_____	( ) _____

Bridal Show Calendar

Contact local bridal publications and associations for information about bridal shows in your area. Take your wedding planner with you and use the pockets to hold brochures and business cards you collect from wedding professionals.

Bridal association _____ Phone ( ) _____

Bridal publication _____ Phone ( ) _____

Month	Date	Time	Location
January			
February			
March			
April			
May			
June			
July			
August			
September			
October			
November			
December			

Marriage License Checklist ————————————————

Look in your local phone book under "County Government/County Clerk's Office" and call to get the following marriage license information:

LOCAL MARRIAGE LICENSE OFFICE

Address_____

Phone_____

Contact_____

Hours open _____

Appointment date_____ Time _____

COST

License fee $_____

Certified copies of your license are available for $_____ per copy

Will accept: ❏ Cash ❏ Check ❏ Money Order ❏ MasterCard ❏ Visa

REQUIREMENTS

Age requirements: bride_____ groom_____

Residence requirements _____

Waiting period before license is issued _____

Waiting period after license is issued _____

Marriage license, once issued, must be used within _____days

Blood test requirements_____

DOCUMENTS NEEDED

❏ Proof of age / ID
❏ Proof of citizenship
❏ Proof of divorce
❏ Doctor's certificate
❏ Letters of parental consent for marriage of minors

Bridal Shopping Checklist ————

Here's a checklist of wedding supplies, bridal accessories and keepsake items that you might want to include in your wedding. Most items are available at bridal salons, stationery stores and rental or party supply stores.

WEDDING STATIONERY

Need	Have	Item	Quantity	Cost	Total
❑	❑	Announcements			
❑	❑	Invitations			
❑	❑	Respond cards/ envelopes			
❑	❑	Pew cards			
❑	❑	At home cards			
❑	❑	Informals			
❑	❑	Wedding programs			
❑	❑	Map cards			
❑	❑	Calligraphy pen			

ITEMS FOR THE CEREMONY

Need	Have	Item	Quantity	Cost	Total
❑	❑	Candles			
❑	❑	Candles: Unity			
❑	❑	Candelabra			
❑	❑	Aisle runner			
❑	❑	Pew bows			
❑	❑	Flower girl basket			
❑	❑	Bride's purse			
❑	❑	Ring bearer pillow			
❑	❑	Garter			
❑	❑	Sixpence for bride's shoe			

Pre-Wedding Activities

OTHER WEDDING ITEMS

Need	Have	Item	Quantity	Cost	Total
❑	❑	Bridal gown cover	_____	_____	_____
❑	❑	Train ring	_____	_____	_____
❑	❑	Keepsake video case	_____	_____	_____
❑	❑	Marriage certificate	_____	_____	_____
❑	❑	Car decorating kit	_____	_____	_____
❑	❑	Photo book	_____	_____	_____
❑	❑	Gift book	_____	_____	_____
❑	❑	Attendants' gifts	_____	_____	_____

ITEMS FOR THE RECEPTION

Need	Have	Item	Quantity	Cost	Total
❑	❑	Guest register	_____	_____	_____
❑	❑	Register pen and pen holder	_____	_____	_____
❑	❑	Cake knife and server set	_____	_____	_____
❑	❑	Cake top decoration	_____	_____	_____
❑	❑	Cake boxes	_____	_____	_____
❑	❑	Toasting goblets	_____	_____	_____
❑	❑	Disposable cameras	_____	_____	_____
❑	❑	Dollar dance pouch	_____	_____	_____
❑	❑	Guest mementos	_____	_____	_____
❑	❑	Silk floral centerpieces	_____	_____	_____
❑	❑	Table centerpieces	_____	_____	_____
❑	❑	Matches, personalized	_____	_____	_____
❑	❑	Napkins, personalized	_____	_____	_____
❑	❑	Thank-you ribbons	_____	_____	_____

Pre-Wedding Activities

ITEMS FOR THE RECEPTION

Need	Have	Item	Quantity	Cost	Total
❑	❑	Paper streamers	_____	_____	_____
❑	❑	Balloons	_____	_____	_____
❑	❑	Confetti	_____	_____	_____
❑	❑	Candles	_____	_____	_____
❑	❑	*Just Married* banners	_____	_____	_____
❑	❑	Servers' aprons	_____	_____	_____
❑	❑	Table covers	_____	_____	_____
❑	❑	Table skirts	_____	_____	_____
❑	❑	Disposable tableware	_____	_____	_____
❑	❑	Flatware	_____	_____	_____
❑	❑	Drinkware	_____	_____	_____
❑	❑	Punch cups	_____	_____	_____
❑	❑	Coasters	_____	_____	_____
❑	❑	Stir sticks	_____	_____	_____
❑	❑	Reception sneakers: lace, pearl, venise style & matching sun visor	_____	_____	_____
❑	❑	Bubbles, rice, birdseed, flower petals to toss	_____	_____	_____
❑	❑	_____	_____	_____	_____
❑	❑	_____	_____	_____	_____
❑	❑	_____	_____	_____	_____
❑	❑	_____	_____	_____	_____
❑	❑	_____	_____	_____	_____
❑	❑	_____	_____	_____	_____
❑	❑	_____	_____	_____	_____
❑	❑	_____	_____	_____	_____
❑	❑	_____	_____	_____	_____

Pre-Wedding Activities Checklist ———————

Due Date   **To Do**

❏ _____ Purchase rings
       ❏ Engagement ring   ❏ Wedding rings

❏ _____ Announce your engagement
       ❏ Newspaper announcement
       ❏ Engagement party
          ❏ Set a budget
          ❏ Find a location
          ❏ Decide on the date and time
          ❏ Plan the menu
          ❏ Choose the decorations
          ❏ Invite the guests

❏ _____ Plan the ceremony rehearsal
       ❏ Decide on the date and time
       ❏ Confirm with the ceremony site
       ❏ Confirm with your officiant
       ❏ Inform the bridal party

❏ _____ Plan the rehearsal dinner party
       ❏ Set a budget
       ❏ Find a location
       ❏ Decide on the date and time
       ❏ Plan the menu
       ❏ Choose the decorations
       ❏ Invite the guests

❏ _____ Host the bridesmaids' luncheon
       ❏ Set a budget
       ❏ Find a location
       ❏ Decide on the date and time
       ❏ Plan the menu
       ❏ Choose the decorations
       ❏ Invite the guests
       ❏ Present attendants with their thank-you gifts

❏ _____ Complete the bridal shower guest list and give a copy
       to the hostess. See: *Bridal Shower Guest and Gift List*

❏ _____ Attend your bridal shower party

❏ _____ Make beauty appointments

❏ _____ Send thank-you notes to the hosts of your pre-wedding parties

Pre-Wedding Parties

❏ ENGAGEMENT PARTY

The engagement party is generally hosted by the bride's parents, but can be hosted by you and your fiancé. The party can be a brunch, luncheon, cocktail party or dinner. Gifts are usually not given.

Date _____ Time _____ Hosted by _____

Location _____

❏ BRIDAL SHOWER

The bridal shower is usually given a month or two before the wedding and is hosted by the maid of honor, a relative or the bridesmaids.

Date _____ Time _____ Hosted by _____

Location _____

❏ BRIDESMAIDS' LUNCHEON

The bridesmaids' luncheon is usually held the month before the wedding and is hosted by the bride-to-be to recognize and honor her attendants. This is a good time to give the bridesmaids and maid of honor their gifts.

Date _____ Time _____ Hosted by _____

Location _____

❏ BACHELOR PARTY

The bachelor party is usually hosted by the best man and/or the groomsmen. The groom may also use this gathering as time to present his attendants with their gifts. Hint: see if the party can be held a few days or a week before the wedding, and not the night before.

Date _____ Time _____ Hosted by _____

Location _____

❏ REHEARSAL DINNER

The rehearsal dinner is usually held after the ceremony rehearsal, and is hosted by the groom's parents. Guests include:
- All members of the wedding party and their spouses or dates
- Children in the wedding and their parents
- The officiant and their spouse
- Members of the bride's and groom's immediate families
- Out-of-town guests who will be staying overnight prior to the wedding

Date _____ Time _____ Hosted by _____

Location _____

Pre-Wedding Activities

Engagement Party Worksheet ————————————

Location _____

Address _____

Phone _____ Contact _____ ❏ Confirmed

Party Date _____ **Time:** from _____ to _____

Date to give final guest count _____ Number of guests _____

Party hosted by _____

Menu and Beverages:

_____

_____

_____

Notes: (decorations/rental equipment)

_____

_____

_____

Cost

Budget _____ Actual _____

Paid by: ❏ Credit Card ❏ Check ❏ Cash

Cost per person _____ Tax _____ Gratuity _____

Deposit _____ Date due _____ ❏ Deposit paid

Balance _____ Date due _____ ❏ Balance paid

Cancellation policy _____

_____   _____

Service Representative Signature   Date

_____   _____

Bridal Party Signature   Date

Use this worksheet as an agreement form and have the service representative sign and date it.

Engagement Party Guest List —————————————

RSVP

Yes   No

❑   ❑   **Name** _____
         Address _____ Phone _____

❑   ❑   **Name** _____
         Address _____ Phone _____

❑   ❑   **Name** _____
         Address _____ Phone _____

❑   ❑   **Name** _____
         Address _____ Phone _____

❑   ❑   **Name** _____
         Address _____ Phone _____

❑   ❑   **Name** _____
         Address _____ Phone _____

❑   ❑   **Name** _____
         Address _____ Phone _____

❑   ❑   **Name** _____
         Address _____ Phone _____

❑   ❑   **Name** _____
         Address _____ Phone _____

❑   ❑   **Name** _____
         Address _____ Phone _____

Please make duplicate copies if necessary

Bridal Luncheon Worksheet ————————————

Location _____

Address _____

Phone _____ Contact _____ ❑ Confirmed

Party Date _____ **Time:** from_____ to _____

Date to give final guest count _____ Number of guests _____

Party hosted by _____

Menu and Beverages:

_____

_____

_____

Notes: (decorations/rental equipment)

_____

_____

_____

Cost

Budget _____ Actual _____

Paid by: ❑ Credit Card   ❑ Check   ❑ Cash

Cost per person _____ Tax _____ Gratuity _____

Deposit _____ Date due _____ ❑ Deposit paid

Balance _____ Date due _____ ❑ Balance paid

Cancellation policy _____

———————————————   ———————————————
Service Representative Signature   Date

———————————————   ———————————————
Bridal Party Signature   Date

Use this worksheet as an agreement form and have the service representative sign and date it.

Pre-Wedding Activities

Bridal Luncheon Guest List ——————————

RSVP

Yes No

❏ ❏ **Name** _____
       Address _____ Phone _____

❏ ❏ **Name** _____
       Address _____ Phone _____

❏ ❏ **Name** _____
       Address _____ Phone _____

❏ ❏ **Name** _____
       Address _____ Phone _____

❏ ❏ **Name** _____
       Address _____ Phone _____

❏ ❏ **Name** _____
       Address _____ Phone _____

❏ ❏ **Name** _____
       Address _____ Phone _____

❏ ❏ **Name** _____
       Address _____ Phone _____

❏ ❏ **Name** _____
       Address _____ Phone _____

❏ ❏ **Name** _____
       Address _____ Phone _____

Please make duplicate copies if necessary

Bridal Shower Guest and Gift List ―――――――――

Give a completed copy of this list to your bridal shower hostess so she can send out invitations. Take this form to the shower and have someone record the gifts you receive so you can send thank-you notes.

Shower date _____ Time _____ Theme _____

Hosted by _____ Phone _____

Location _____

RSVP

Yes　No

❑　❑　**Name** _____
　　　　Address _____ Phone _____
　　　　Gift _____ ❑ Thank-you sent

❑　❑　**Name** _____
　　　　Address _____ Phone _____
　　　　Gift _____ ❑ Thank-you sent

❑　❑　**Name** _____
　　　　Address _____ Phone _____
　　　　Gift _____ ❑ Thank-you sent

❑　❑　**Name** _____
　　　　Address _____ Phone _____
　　　　Gift _____ ❑ Thank-you sent

❑　❑　**Name** _____
　　　　Address _____ Phone _____
　　　　Gift _____ ❑ Thank-you sent

❑　❑　**Name** _____
　　　　Address _____ Phone _____
　　　　Gift _____ ❑ Thank-you sent

Pre-Wedding Activities

RSVP

Yes No

❑ ❑ **Name** _____
Address _____ Phone _____
Gift _____ ❑ Thank-you sent

❑ ❑ **Name** _____
Address _____ Phone _____
Gift _____ ❑ Thank-you sent

❑ ❑ **Name** _____
Address _____ Phone _____
Gift _____ ❑ Thank-you sent

❑ ❑ **Name** _____
Address _____ Phone _____
Gift _____ ❑ Thank-you sent

❑ ❑ **Name** _____
Address _____ Phone _____
Gift _____ ❑ Thank-you sent

❑ ❑ **Name** _____
Address _____ Phone _____
Gift _____ ❑ Thank-you sent

❑ ❑ **Name** _____
Address _____ Phone _____
Gift _____ ❑ Thank-you sent

❑ ❑ **Name** _____
Address _____ Phone _____
Gift _____ ❑ Thank-you sent

❑ ❑ **Name** _____
Address _____ Phone _____
Gift _____ ❑ Thank-you sent

Please make duplicate copies if necessary

Wedding Rehearsal Checklist ——————————————

Wedding Rehearsal Location _____

Address _____

Phone_____ Contact _____ ❑ Confirmed

Date of rehearsal_____ Time: from _____ to _____

To Do

❑ Make arrangements for the ceremony rehearsal with the officiant at the same time you set the date for your wedding. The rehearsal is usually held the evening before the wedding, with a dinner party afterwards.

Attendees

Invite everyone involved in the ceremony to attend the rehearsal.
- ❑ Officiant and spouse or guest
- ❑ Wedding coordinator and spouse or date
- ❑ Bride's parents
- ❑ Groom's parents
- ❑ Maid of honor and spouse or date
- ❑ Best man and spouse or date
- ❑ Bridesmaids and their spouses or dates
- ❑ Flower girl and her parents
- ❑ Groomsmen and their spouses or dates
- ❑ Ring bearer and his parents
- ❑ Musicians/vocalist and their spouses or dates

Supplies

Following is a list of items you may need at the wedding rehearsal.

Need	Have	
❑	❑	This wedding planner
❑	❑	Camera and film
❑	❑	Wedding coordinator's checklist
❑	❑	Copies of the wedding and reception timeline
❑	❑	Copies of your wedding vows
❑	❑	Practice wedding bouquet
❑	❑	Maps or directions to the rehearsal dinner
❑	❑	Marriage license
❑	❑	Gifts for attendants

Selecting a Rehearsal Dinner Site ———————

Estimate #1

Appointment date _____ Time _____

Business _____

Address _____

_____

Contact _____

Phone _____

_____

Rehearsal dinner budget $ _____

Estimated total cost $ _____

Deposit required $ _____

Cancellation policy _____

❑ Viewed site/room where party would be held.

❑ Picked up price list and brochure.

QUESTIONS TO ASK

What dates are available? _____

What times are available? _____

Minimum/maximum # of guests allowed? _____

What is the room size and decor? _____

Is it handicapped accessible? _____

What are your parking facilities? _____

PRICES

Room rental fee _____

Food cost per-person _____

Beverage cost per-person _____

Gratuity and taxes _____

Parking fee/valet service fee _____

MENU ITEMS

_____

_____

_____

_____

_____

_____

_____

_____

_____

_____

_____

Please make duplicate copies if necessary

Selecting a Rehearsal Dinner Site ————

Estimate #2

Appointment date _____ Time _____

Business _____

Address _____

_____

Contact _____

Phone_____

_____

Rehearsal dinner budget $ _____

Estimated total cost $ _____

Deposit required $ _____

Cancellation policy _____

❏ Viewed site/room where party would be held.

❏ Picked up price list and brochure.

QUESTIONS TO ASK

What dates are available? _____

What times are available? _____

Minimum/maximum # of guests allowed? _____

What is the room size and decor? _____

Is it handicapped accessible? _____

What are your parking facilities? _____

PRICES

Room rental fee _____

Food cost per-person _____

Beverage cost per-person _____

Gratuity and taxes _____

Parking fee/valet service fee _____

MENU ITEMS

_____

_____

_____

_____

_____

_____

_____

_____

_____

_____

_____

Please make duplicate copies if necessary

Rehearsal Dinner Worksheet ——————————————

Location _____

Address _____

Phone _____ Contact _____ ❑ Confirmed

Party Date_____ Time: from _____ to _____

Date to give final guest count_____ Number of guests _____

Party hosted by _____

Menu and Beverages:

_____

_____

_____

Notes: (decorations/rental equipment)

_____

_____

_____

Cost

Budget _____ Actual _____

Paid by: ❑ Credit Card   ❑ Check   ❑ Cash

Cost per person _____ Tax _____ Gratuity _____

Deposit _____ Date due _____ ❑ Deposit paid

Balance_____ Date due _____ ❑ Balance paid

Cancellation policy _____

_____   _____
Service Representative Signature   Date

_____   _____
Bridal Party Signature   Date

Use this worksheet as an agreement form and have the service representative sign and date it.

Beauty Worksheet _____

Salon _____

Address_____

Phone _____ Contact _____ ❏ Confirmed

Cost

Budget _____ Actual _____

Paid by: ❏ Credit Card   ❏ Check   ❏ Cash

Appointment cancellation policy _____

Service	Appointment Date and Time	Cost
Facial	_____	_____
Hair cut & style	_____	_____
Hair color	_____	_____
Hair removal (waxing...)	_____	_____
Makeover/Makeup	_____	_____
Manicure	_____	_____
Massage	_____	_____
Pedicure	_____	_____
Perm	_____	_____
Style hair with veil	_____	_____
Tanning	_____	_____
_____	_____	_____
_____	_____	_____
_____	_____	_____
Total		$ _____

The Wedding Party

Selecting Your Wedding Party

You and the groom select your own attendants, usually six to nine months before the wedding.

The formal wedding generally consists of:
* Maid and/or matron of honor
* Best man
* Bridesmaids
* Groomsmen/Ushers
* Parents
* Flower girl
* Ring bearer and/or train bearer

The maid or matron of honor is usually someone you feel close to, such as a sister or best friend. It is acceptable to have both a maid and matron of honor. (A matron of honor is a married friend, sister, relative, etc.)

Generally the best man is the groom's brother, best friend or close relative; it could also be the groom's father or son.

The bridesmaids are usually close friends or sisters of the bride or groom.

As a general rule, you should have one usher for every fifty guests, they are usually brothers, close friends or relatives of the bride or groom.

Flower girls usually range in age from four to nine. Be sure to check with your ceremony site if you want her to scatter rose petals down the aisle.

Ring bearers and/or train bearers are usually four to eight years of age.

Attendants' Duties

The following pages list the traditional responsibilities of your attendants. Use these pages to add any additional duties you would like particular individuals to take care of. Provide a copy to each of your attendants.

Attendants' Information

The *Information for the Bridesmaids* and *Information for the Groomsmen* pages list important information your attendants need to know, such as parties and events they should attend, the wedding and reception date, time, location, transportation information and a wedding day checklist. Give a copy to each of your attendants.

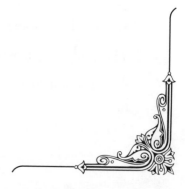

Gifts for the Wedding Party

The bride and groom traditionally present members of the wedding party with a small gift, as a token of appreciation and as a keepsake of the wedding. Bridesmaids' gifts are usually given at the bridesmaids' luncheon, or the rehearsal dinner. The ushers' gifts can be given at the bachelor party or the rehearsal dinner.

BRIDESMAIDS' GIFT IDEAS:
Silk floral keepsake bouquet, heart-shaped keepsake box with an item of jewelry they can wear in the wedding, engraved letter opener, music box, picture frame, tickets to the theater, ballet or a sporting event, magazine subscription, gift certificate at a beauty salon for a day of beauty, a facial, manicure or pedicure, or a massage, gift certificate to a women's store or a bookstore.

USHERS' GIFT IDEAS:
Engraved mugs, engraved pen, engraved business card holder, engraved money clips, cuff links, desk clock, leather wallets, tickets to a sporting event, magazine subscription, gift certificate to a men's store or sports store, travel kits.

FLOWER GIRL AND RING BEARER:
Present each child with a framed photograph of the wedding party as a keepsake gift.

Name	Gift

Wedding Party Checklist ——————————

Due Date   **To Do**

❑ _____   Select the members of your wedding party:

   ❑ Maid of honor
   ❑ Matron of honor
   ❑ Best man
   ❑ Flower girl
   ❑ Ring bearer
   ❑ Train bearer
   ❑ Bridesmaids

   _____

   _____

   ❑ Groomsmen/Ushers

   _____

   _____

❑ _____   Record the names, addresses and phone numbers of the wedding party members in the *Wedding Directory* section.

❑ _____   Make copies of the *Attendants' Duties* pages and give to each member.

❑ _____   Fill in the *Information for the Bridesmaids* and *Information for the Groomsmen* pages and give copies to each member.

❑ _____   Inform wedding party members of the ceremony rehearsal details.

❑ _____   Invite wedding party members to the rehearsal dinner party.

❑ _____   Purchase gifts for your attendants:

   ❑ Maid of honor
   ❑ Each bridesmaid
   ❑ Flower girl
   ❑ Best man
   ❑ Each usher
   ❑ Ring bearer

The Wedding Party

Duties of the Maid of Honor

These are the traditional responsibilities of the maid of honor:

BEFORE THE WEDDING

- Plans and coordinates the shower, either alone or with the bridesmaids.
- Pays for her own wedding attire and accessories.
- Helps coordinate the bridesmaids with their fittings.
- Helps with addressing invitations, shopping and planning.
- Attends the ceremony rehearsal and is invited to the rehearsal dinner party.

BEFORE THE CEREMONY

- Helps the bride get ready before the ceremony.
- Oversees the bridesmaids and informs them of their responsibilities.
- Responsible for holding the groom's wedding ring until the appropriate time in the ceremony.

DURING THE CEREMONY

- Arranges the bride's veil and train during the ceremony.
- Holds the bride's bouquet during the ceremony.
- At the appropriate time in the ceremony she hands the officiant the groom's wedding ring.

AFTER THE CEREMONY

- Signs the marriage certificate as a legal witness.

DURING THE RECEPTION

- Stands next to the groom in the receiving line, if there is one.
- Sits next to the groom at the bridal table.
- Dances with the best man during the traditional first dance.

AFTER THE RECEPTION

- Helps the bride change into her going-away clothes after the reception.

Give a copy of this page to the maid of honor.

Duties of the Bridesmaids

These are the traditional responsibilities of the bridesmaids:

BEFORE THE WEDDING

- Pay for their own wedding attire and accessories.
- Can help out, when needed, with pre-wedding preparations.
- May co-host the bridal shower with the maid of honor.
- Attend the ceremony rehearsal and are invited to the rehearsal dinner party.

BEFORE THE CEREMONY

- Bridesmaids will be escorted by the groomsmen/ushers during the:
  ❑ Processional   ❑ Recessional   ❑ Both

DURING THE CEREMONY

- Sit next to their groomsmen/usher partner during the reception.
- Dance with their groomsmen/usher partner during the traditional first dance.

Duties of the Flower Girl

- The flower girl's parents are usually responsible for her attire.
- She usually carries a basket of flowers or a small nosegay.
- She usually walks before the bride in the processional, stands next to the maid or matron of honor during the ceremony and follows the bride and groom during the recessional.
- During the reception she sits with her family.

Duties of the Ring Bearer or Train Bearer

- The parents are usually responsible for the boys' attire.
- The ring bearer usually carries a cushion with two fake rings tied to it. He walks down the aisle either before the flower girl or next to her.
- The train bearer carries the bridal gown train, following the bride down the aisle.
- During the reception he sits with his family.

**Give a copy of this page to the bridesmaids
and the flower girl and ring bearer's parents.**

Duties of the Best Man

These are the traditional responsibilities of the best man:

BEFORE THE WEDDING

- Plans and coordinates the bachelor party.
- Pays for his own wedding attire and accessories.
- Helps coordinate the groomsmen's formal wear fitting.
- Assists the groom with wedding and honeymoon travel preparations.
- Attends the ceremony rehearsal and is invited to the rehearsal dinner party.

BEFORE THE CEREMONY

- Gets the groom to the ceremony site on time: _____A.M./P.M.
- Holds the bride's wedding ring until the appropriate time in the ceremony.
- Oversees the groomsmen/ushers and informs them of their responsibilities.

DURING THE CEREMONY

- At the appropriate time in the ceremony he hands the officiant the bride's wedding ring.

AFTER THE CEREMONY

- Signs the marriage certificate as a legal witness.
- Responsible for giving the officiant the honorarium (which he should receive from the groom in a sealed envelope).

DURING THE RECEPTION

- Stands next to the bride in the receiving line, if there is one.
- Sits to the right of the bride at the bridal table.
- Offers the first toast to the bride and groom at the reception.
- Dances with the maid of honor during the traditional first dance.

AFTER THE RECEPTION

- Makes sure that the "getaway" car is ready to go, the luggage is locked inside and the groom has travel documents in order.
- Returns the groom's attire to the rental shop.

Give a copy of this page to the best man.

Duties of the Groomsmen/Ushers

These are the traditional responsibilities of the groomsmen/ushers:

BEFORE THE WEDDING

- Pay for their own wedding attire and accessories.
- Attend the ceremony rehearsal and are invited to the rehearsal dinner party.

BEFORE THE CEREMONY

- Arrive at the wedding site early to seat any early guests.
  Please arrive by: A.M./P.M. _____
- Should be prepared to direct guests to parking and restroom facilities, as well as the reception site.
- The first _____ rows on each side are reserved for immediate family.
- Start seating guests as soon as they arrive. They should offer female guests their right arm, and follow men down the aisle unless they are elderly or handicapped. If a group of guests arrive at the same time, seat the eldest guests first.
- Traditionally the bride's guests sit on the left side and the groom's sit on the right (reverse for an Orthodox Jewish ceremony). Ask the guest which side she should be seated on. (It is acceptable to divide them evenly on either side.)

IMMEDIATELY PRIOR TO THE CEREMONY

- Seat the mother of the groom in the right front row (approx. five minutes before the mother of the bride), then seat the bride's mother in the left front row. She is the last person to be seated before the processional begins.
- Unroll the aisle runner (if applicable), then take their place.
- The groomsmen will be escorting the bridesmaids during the:
  ❑ Processional   ❑ Recessional   ❑ Both

DURING THE RECEPTION

- Sits next to their bridesmaid partner during the reception.
- Dances with their bridesmaid partner during the traditional first dance.

Give a copy of this page to the groomsmen.

The Wedding Party

Information for the Maid of Honor and Bridesmaids —

IMPORTANT PHONE NUMBERS

Bride _____ Groom _____

Bride's Parents _____ Groom's Parents _____

Other _____

ATTIRE FITTING DATES

First Fitting: Final Fitting:

Date _____ Time _____   Date _____ Time _____

Location _____

PRE-WEDDING PARTIES

Date _____ Time _____ Occasion _____

Location _____

Date _____ Time _____ Occasion _____

Location _____

THE REHEARSAL

Date _____ Time _____ Location _____

THE REHEARSAL DINNER

Date _____ Time _____ Location _____

THE WEDDING

Date _____ Arrival time _____ Location _____

_____

Where to dress _____

Transportation _____

The Wedding Party

THE RECEPTION

Location _____

Transportation _____

PLEASE BE AVAILABLE FOR PICTURES:

❑ Before the ceremony: Time _____ Location _____
❑ After the ceremony
❑ Both

WEDDING DAY CHECKLIST

❑ Dress
❑ Headpiece
❑ Slip
❑ Gloves
❑ Shoes
❑ Hosiery
❑ Jewelry
❑ Makeup
❑ Nail polish
❑ Mirror
❑ Hairpins
❑ Brush/Comb
❑ Hairspray
❑ Perfume
❑ Breath mints

**Fill in this form and give a copy to the maid of honor and
each of the bridesmaids.**

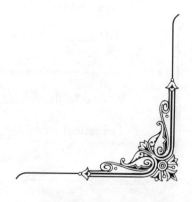

The Wedding Party

Information for the Best Man and Groomsmen

IMPORTANT PHONE NUMBERS

Bride_____ Groom _____

Bride's Parents_____ Groom's Parents _____

Other _____

ATTIRE FITTING DATES

First Fitting: Final Fitting:

Date _____Time _____   Date _____Time _____

Location _____

PRE-WEDDING PARTIES

Date _____ Time _____ Occasion _____

Location _____

Date _____Time _____ Occasion _____

Location _____

THE REHEARSAL

Date _____Time _____Location _____

THE REHEARSAL DINNER

Date _____Time _____Location _____

THE WEDDING

Date _____ Arrival time _____Location _____

_____

Where to dress _____

Transportation _____

The Wedding Party

THE RECEPTION

Location _____

Transportation _____

PLEASE BE AVAILABLE FOR PICTURES:

❑ Before the ceremony: Time _____ Location _____

❑ After the ceremony

❑ Both

WEDDING DAY CHECKLIST

❑ Coat

❑ Trousers

❑ Shirt

❑ Vest

❑ Tie/Ascot

❑ Gloves

❑ Cummerbund

❑ Shoes

❑ Socks

❑ Suspenders

❑ Cufflinks

❑ Brush/Comb

❑ Hairspray

❑ Cologne

❑ Breath mints

Fill in this form and give a copy to the best man and each of the groomsmen.

Guests and Gifts

Wedding Invitations

WEDDING INVITATION TIPS

Estimate the size of your guest list as soon as possible. To organize your list, ask your fiancé, his parents and your parents to submit a list of the people they would like to invite. Include your names, and compare lists. Cross off any duplications and add up the names that are left. Compare this amount with your estimated guest count. If the list is over the limit, decide how many names need to be eliminated and have each person delete a certain number of names. Remember, the size of your guest list will affect the total cost of your wedding.

The invitation package you select will be a reflection of you and lets your guests know what type of wedding you are having. Your stationer will be able to help you sort through the many styles available and answer questions regarding the appropriate invitation wording. The following pages show sample wordings to help you get started.

ORDERING YOUR INVITATIONS

Order your invitations four to six months before the wedding. The printer may need four weeks to process the order, and you should allow a month to address them. Mail them out four to six weeks before the wedding.

When determining how many invitations to order, figure one invitation per couple, one for each single guest and their date, and one for children over age eighteen in

a family. Also, one for your officiant, attendants and their dates, and both sets of parents. Order more invitations than you think you will need, and order extra envelopes for mistakes.

Ask if you can receive the envelopes before the invitations arrive so you can start addressing them.

Proofread the order carefully. Also, proofread the stationery when you pick up the finished product, before leaving the stationer.

ADDRESSING AND ASSEMBLING THE INVITATIONS

First address both the inner and outer envelopes and get your invitations ready to be inserted.

Allow plenty of time if you are hiring a professional calligrapher to address the envelopes. If your guest list is large, it could take about two weeks for the calligrapher to do your invitations.

Invitations are folded with the printed surface on the outside. Enclosures can either be placed inside the fold, or laid face up on top of the invitation in order of importance: reply card, reception card, etc.

Insert the invitation and enclosures into the ungummed inner envelope, folded edge first with the text facing the back of the envelope. The inner envelope is addressed formally as "Mr. and Mrs. Cameron" (first names are omitted), without an address. If children are invited, list their names below that of their parents on the inner envelope only.

Insert the inner envelope into the outer envelope. The side of the inner envelope that has names on it should face the back of the outer, gummed envelope. The guests' names should be seen when the envelope is opened. Seal the outer envelope.

MAILING THE INVITATIONS

The invitation packet will require additional postage. Take a completely assembled invitation to the post office before you purchase the stamps to determine the correct amount of postage needed.

Purchase peel-off stamps with a special design and be sure to buy enough for the response envelopes as well.

Invitations should be mailed out no more than six weeks, but not less than four weeks before the ceremony, so your guests have time to reply. Choose an RSVP date that is not less than two weeks before the wedding.

Ask the postmaster to hand-cancel your invitations.

THANK-YOU NOTES

Send thank-you notes for gifts received before the wedding, within three weeks. For gifts received on or after your wedding day, send thank-you notes within three months

For special thank-yous, enclose a candid photo from your wedding reception. Be sure to order thank-you notes that will accommodate the size of the photo.

Record the gifts you receive, and when the thank-you notes have been sent, under the appropriate name on the *Wedding Guest and Gift List* pages.

Wedding Invitation Examples

BRIDE'S PARENTS HOSTING:

Mr. and Mrs. Harold A. Andersen
request the honour of your presence
at the marriage of their daughter
Ann Marie
to
Mr. Michael Hume Cameron
Saturday, the twenty third of April
at half after seven o'clock
First Methodist Church
1212 Oak Street
Portland, Oregon

WEDDING HELD AT THE HOME OF A FRIEND

Substitute in Place of Church the Following Wording:

at the residence of
Mr. and Mrs. Steven Donner
2328 Kinzalow Drive
Portland, Oregon

GROOM'S PARENTS HOSTING:

Mr. and Mrs. Steven Cameron
request the honour of your presence
at the marriage of
Ann Marie Andersen
to their son
Michael Hume Cameron

etc.

BRIDE AND GROOM HOSTING:

Miss Ann Marie Andersen
and
Mr. Michael Hume Cameron
request the honour of your presence
at their marriage
etc.

Divorced Parents

BRIDE'S REMARRIED MOTHER HOSTING:

Mr. and Mrs. Brandon Forys
request the honour of your presence
at the marriage of her daughter

Divorced Parents

BRIDE'S REMARRIED FATHER HOSTING:

Mr. and Mrs. Harold A. Andersen
request the honour of your presence
at the marriage of his daughter

WHEN THE BRIDE'S UNMARRIED MOTHER HOSTS, SHE USES HER MAIDEN AND MARRIED NAME:

Mrs. Anna Spisla Andersen
requests the honour of your presence
at the marriage of her daughter

RECEPTION INVITATION:

Mr. and Mrs. Harold A. Andersen
request the pleasure of your company
at the wedding reception
honoring their daughter
Ann Marie
and
Michael Hume Cameron
etc.

RECEPTION CARD:
(to accompany a formal invitation)

Dinner and Dance Reception
following ceremony
Red Lion Hotel
Rose Room
3246 Oak Street
Portland, Oregon

RECEPTION CARD:
(to accompany a formal invitation)

Buffet Reception
immediately following ceremony
in Church Hall

RESPONSE CARD:

Please respond on or before
March 23, 1998

M _____

Number of persons _____

RESPONSE CARD:

The favor of a reply is requested
on or before March 23, 1998

M _____

_____will attend

PLACE CARD:

Ann and Michael
April 23, 1998

_____

Table No._____

PEW CARD:

Ann Marie and Michael
First Methodist Church
Bride's Section

Pew Number_____

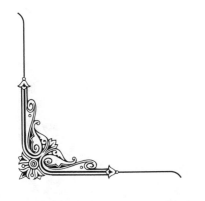

Guests and Gifts

Invitations Checklist

Due Date   **To Do**

❑ _____   Compile names and addresses of guests as soon as possible:
    ❑ Bride's guest list
    ❑ Groom's guest list
    ❑ Bride's parents' guest list
    ❑ Groom's parents' guest list

❑ _____   Finalize the guest list and determine the number of invites to order.

❑ _____   Order the invitations and stationery:
    ❑ Invitations
    ❑ Enclosures:
      ____ Response cards
      ____ Reception cards
      ____ Pew cards
      ____ Church cards
      ____ Maps
    ❑ Wedding programs
    ❑ Announcements
    ❑ At home cards
    ❑ Stationery:
      ____ Thank-you notes
      ____ Personal stationery
    ❑ Miscellaneous:
      ____ Place cards
      ____ Personalized party items: napkins, matchbooks, etc.

❑ _____   Double-check all spellings, dates and addresses on your order.
❑ _____   Design and print maps to be inserted with the invitation.
❑ _____   Address and assemble the invitations.
❑ _____   Weigh the invitation packets to ensure proper postage.
❑ _____   Purchase stamps.
❑ _____   Mail the invitations.
❑ _____   Mail the announcements.
❑ _____   Write thank-you notes.
❑ _____   Mail thank-you notes.

Invitations Worksheet —————————————————

Stationer _____

Address_____

Phone _____ Contact_____ ❏ Confirmed

Cost

Invitations _____ Envelopes _____ Liners _____

Response cards_____ Envelopes _____

Reception cards _____ Pew cards _____

Announcements _____ Wedding programs _____

Place cards _____ Thank-you notes _____

Other _____

_____

Invitations

Quantity ordered _____ Date ordered _____ Delivery date _____

Style _____ Typestyle _____

Paper _____ Color _____ Ink color _____

Wording

Name of hosts _____

Request _____

Bride and groom _____

Day and date _____

Time _____

Location _____

Corner copy _____

Envelopes

❏ Unlined   ❏ Lined: Color _____

Guests and Gifts

Preprinted return address _____
_____
_____
_____

Response cards _____
_____
_____

Address for response cards _____
_____
_____
_____

Reception cards _____
_____
_____
_____

Pew cards _____
_____
_____

At-home cards _____
_____
_____

Place cards _____
_____
_____

Thank-you cards _____
_____
_____

Announcements _____
_____
_____

Wedding Guest and Gift List ———————————

RSVP

Yes   No

❑   ❑   **Name** _____

Address _____

❑ Bride   ❑ Groom   ❑ Friend   ❑ Family

\# Ceremony _____   \# Reception _____

Gift _____ ❑ Thank-you sent

❑   ❑   **Name** _____

Address _____

❑ Bride   ❑ Groom   ❑ Friend   ❑ Family

\# Ceremony _____   \# Reception _____

Gift _____ ❑ Thank-you sent

❑   ❑   **Name** _____

Address _____

❑ Bride   ❑ Groom   ❑ Friend   ❑ Family

\# Ceremony _____   \# Reception _____

Gift _____ ❑ Thank-you sent

❑   ❑   **Name** _____

Address _____

❑ Bride   ❑ Groom   ❑ Friend   ❑ Family

\# Ceremony _____   \# Reception _____

Gift _____ ❑ Thank-you sent

Guests and Gifts

RSVP

Yes No

❏ ❏ **Name** _____
Address _____
_____
❏ Bride ❏ Groom ❏ Friend ❏ Family
Ceremony _____ # Reception _____
Gift _____ ❏ Thank-you sent

❏ ❏ **Name** _____
Address _____
_____
❏ Bride ❏ Groom ❏ Friend ❏ Family
Ceremony _____ # Reception _____
Gift _____ ❏ Thank-you sent

❏ ❏ **Name** _____
Address _____
_____
❏ Bride ❏ Groom ❏ Friend ❏ Family
Ceremony _____ # Reception _____
Gift _____ ❏ Thank-you sent

❏ ❏ **Name** _____
Address _____
_____
❏ Bride ❏ Groom ❏ Friend ❏ Family
Ceremony _____ # Reception _____
Gift _____ ❏ Thank-you sent

❏ ❏ **Name** _____
Address _____
_____
❏ Bride ❏ Groom ❏ Friend ❏ Family
Ceremony _____ # Reception _____
Gift _____ ❏ Thank-you sent

Guests and Gifts

RSVP

Yes	No
❏	❏

Name _____

Address _____

_____

❏ Bride ❏ Groom ❏ Friend ❏ Family

\# Ceremony _____ # Reception _____

Gift _____ ❏ Thank-you sent

❏	❏

Name _____

Address _____

_____

❏ Bride ❏ Groom ❏ Friend ❏ Family

\# Ceremony _____ # Reception _____

Gift _____ ❏ Thank-you sent

❏	❏

Name _____

Address _____

_____

❏ Bride ❏ Groom ❏ Friend ❏ Family

\# Ceremony _____ # Reception _____

Gift _____ ❏ Thank-you sent

❏	❏

Name _____

Address _____

_____

❏ Bride ❏ Groom ❏ Friend ❏ Family

\# Ceremony _____ # Reception _____

Gift _____ ❏ Thank-you sent

❏	❏

Name _____

Address _____

_____

❏ Bride ❏ Groom ❏ Friend ❏ Family

\# Ceremony _____ # Reception _____

Gift _____ ❏ Thank-you sent

Guests and Gifts

Yes No

❑   ❑   **Name** _____

Address _____

_____

❑ Bride   ❑ Groom   ❑ Friend   ❑ Family

Ceremony _____ # Reception _____

Gift _____ ❑ Thank-you sent

❑   ❑   **Name** _____

Address _____

_____

❑ Bride   ❑ Groom   ❑ Friend   ❑ Family

Ceremony _____ # Reception _____

Gift _____ ❑ Thank-you sent

❑   ❑   **Name** _____

Address _____

_____

❑ Bride   ❑ Groom   ❑ Friend   ❑ Family

Ceremony _____ # Reception _____

Gift _____ ❑ Thank-you sent

❑   ❑   **Name** _____

Address _____

_____

❑ Bride   ❑ Groom   ❑ Friend   ❑ Family

Ceremony _____ # Reception _____

Gift _____ ❑ Thank-you sent

❑   ❑   **Name** _____

Address _____

_____

❑ Bride   ❑ Groom   ❑ Friend   ❑ Family

Ceremony _____ # Reception _____

Gift _____ ❑ Thank-you sent

Guests and Gifts

RSVP

Yes No

❑ ❑ **Name** _____
Address _____
_____
❑ Bride ❑ Groom ❑ Friend ❑ Family
Ceremony _____ # Reception _____
Gift _____ ❑ Thank-you sent

❑ ❑ **Name** _____
Address _____
_____
❑ Bride ❑ Groom ❑ Friend ❑ Family
Ceremony _____ # Reception _____
Gift _____ ❑ Thank-you sent

❑ ❑ **Name** _____
Address _____
_____
❑ Bride ❑ Groom ❑ Friend ❑ Family
Ceremony _____ # Reception _____
Gift _____ ❑ Thank-you sent

❑ ❑ **Name** _____
Address _____
_____
❑ Bride ❑ Groom ❑ Friend ❑ Family
Ceremony _____ # Reception _____
Gift _____ ❑ Thank-you sent

❑ ❑ **Name** _____
Address _____
_____
❑ Bride ❑ Groom ❑ Friend ❑ Family
Ceremony _____ # Reception _____
Gift _____ ❑ Thank-you sent

Guests and Gifts

Yes **No**

❑ ❑ **Name** _____
Address _____
_____
❑ Bride   ❑ Groom   ❑ Friend   ❑ Family
Ceremony _____   # Reception _____
Gift _____ ❑ Thank-you sent

❑ ❑ **Name** _____
Address _____
_____
❑ Bride   ❑ Groom   ❑ Friend   ❑ Family
Ceremony _____   # Reception _____
Gift _____ ❑ Thank-you sent

❑ ❑ **Name** _____
Address _____
_____
❑ Bride   ❑ Groom   ❑ Friend   ❑ Family
Ceremony _____   # Reception _____
Gift _____ ❑ Thank-you sent

❑ ❑ **Name** _____
Address _____
_____
❑ Bride   ❑ Groom   ❑ Friend   ❑ Family
Ceremony _____   # Reception _____
Gift _____ ❑ Thank-you sent

❑ ❑ **Name** _____
Address _____
_____
❑ Bride   ❑ Groom   ❑ Friend   ❑ Family
Ceremony _____   # Reception _____
Gift _____ ❑ Thank-you sent

Guests and Gifts

RSVP

Yes No

☐ ☐ **Name** _____
Address _____
_____
☐ Bride   ☐ Groom   ☐ Friend   ☐ Family
Ceremony _____   # Reception _____
Gift _____   ☐ Thank-you sent

☐ ☐ **Name** _____
Address _____
_____
☐ Bride   ☐ Groom   ☐ Friend   ☐ Family
Ceremony _____   # Reception _____
Gift _____   ☐ Thank-you sent

☐ ☐ **Name** _____
Address _____
_____
☐ Bride   ☐ Groom   ☐ Friend   ☐ Family
Ceremony _____   # Reception _____
Gift _____   ☐ Thank-you sent

☐ ☐ **Name** _____
Address _____
_____
☐ Bride   ☐ Groom   ☐ Friend   ☐ Family
Ceremony _____   # Reception _____
Gift _____   ☐ Thank-you sent

☐ ☐ **Name** _____
Address _____
_____
☐ Bride   ☐ Groom   ☐ Friend   ☐ Family
Ceremony _____   # Reception _____
Gift _____   ☐ Thank-you sent

Guests and Gifts

RSVP

Yes No

❑   ❑   **Name** _____

Address _____

_____

❑ Bride   ❑ Groom   ❑ Friend   ❑ Family

\# Ceremony _____ # Reception _____

Gift _____ ❑ Thank-you sent

❑   ❑   **Name** _____

Address _____

_____

❑ Bride   ❑ Groom   ❑ Friend   ❑ Family

\# Ceremony _____ # Reception _____

Gift _____ ❑ Thank-you sent

❑   ❑   **Name** _____

Address _____

_____

❑ Bride   ❑ Groom   ❑ Friend   ❑ Family

\# Ceremony _____ # Reception _____

Gift _____ ❑ Thank-you sent

❑   ❑   **Name** _____

Address _____

_____

❑ Bride   ❑ Groom   ❑ Friend   ❑ Family

\# Ceremony _____ # Reception _____

Gift _____ ❑ Thank-you sent

❑   ❑   **Name** _____

Address _____

_____

❑ Bride   ❑ Groom   ❑ Friend   ❑ Family

\# Ceremony _____ # Reception _____

Gift _____ ❑ Thank-you sent

Guests and Gifts

Yes **No**

❑ ❑ **Name** _____
Address _____
_____
❑ Bride   ❑ Groom   ❑ Friend   ❑ Family
Ceremony _____ # Reception _____
Gift _____ ❑ Thank-you sent

❑ ❑ **Name** _____
Address _____
_____
❑ Bride   ❑ Groom   ❑ Friend   ❑ Family
Ceremony _____ # Reception _____
Gift _____ ❑ Thank-you sent

❑ ❑ **Name** _____
Address _____
_____
❑ Bride   ❑ Groom   ❑ Friend   ❑ Family
Ceremony _____ # Reception _____
Gift _____ ❑ Thank-you sent

❑ ❑ **Name** _____
Address _____
_____
❑ Bride   ❑ Groom   ❑ Friend   ❑ Family
Ceremony _____ # Reception _____
Gift _____ ❑ Thank-you sent

❑ ❑ **Name** _____
Address _____
_____
❑ Bride   ❑ Groom   ❑ Friend   ❑ Family
Ceremony _____ # Reception _____
Gift _____ ❑ Thank-you sent

Guests and Gifts

Yes **No**

☐ ☐ **Name** _____

Address _____

_____

☐ Bride ☐ Groom ☐ Friend ☐ Family

Ceremony _____ # Reception _____

Gift _____ ☐ Thank-you sent

☐ ☐ **Name** _____

Address _____

_____

☐ Bride ☐ Groom ☐ Friend ☐ Family

Ceremony _____ # Reception _____

Gift _____ ☐ Thank-you sent

☐ ☐ **Name** _____

Address _____

_____

☐ Bride ☐ Groom ☐ Friend ☐ Family

Ceremony _____ # Reception _____

Gift _____ ☐ Thank-you sent

☐ ☐ **Name** _____

Address _____

_____

☐ Bride ☐ Groom ☐ Friend ☐ Family

Ceremony _____ # Reception _____

Gift _____ ☐ Thank-you sent

☐ ☐ **Name** _____

Address _____

_____

☐ Bride ☐ Groom ☐ Friend ☐ Family

Ceremony _____ # Reception _____

Gift _____ ☐ Thank-you sent

Guests and Gifts

RSVP

Yes No

❏ ❏ **Name** _____

Address _____

❏ Bride   ❏ Groom   ❏ Friend   ❏ Family

\# Ceremony _____   \# Reception _____

Gift _____ ❏ Thank-you sent

❏ ❏ **Name** _____

Address _____

❏ Bride   ❏ Groom   ❏ Friend   ❏ Family

\# Ceremony _____   \# Reception _____

Gift _____ ❏ Thank-you sent

❏ ❏ **Name** _____

Address _____

❏ Bride   ❏ Groom   ❏ Friend   ❏ Family

\# Ceremony _____   \# Reception _____

Gift _____ ❏ Thank-you sent

❏ ❏ **Name** _____

Address _____

❏ Bride   ❏ Groom   ❏ Friend   ❏ Family

\# Ceremony _____   \# Reception _____

Gift _____ ❏ Thank-you sent

❏ ❏ **Name** _____

Address _____

❏ Bride   ❏ Groom   ❏ Friend   ❏ Family

\# Ceremony _____   \# Reception _____

Gift _____ ❏ Thank-you sent

Guests and Gifts

RSVP

Yes No

☐ ☐ **Name** _____
Address _____
_____
☐ Bride   ☐ Groom   ☐ Friend   ☐ Family
Ceremony _____ # Reception _____
Gift _____ ☐ Thank-you sent

☐ ☐ **Name** _____
Address _____
_____
☐ Bride   ☐ Groom   ☐ Friend   ☐ Family
Ceremony _____ # Reception _____
Gift _____ ☐ Thank-you sent

☐ ☐ **Name** _____
Address _____
_____
☐ Bride   ☐ Groom   ☐ Friend   ☐ Family
Ceremony _____ # Reception _____
Gift _____ ☐ Thank-you sent

☐ ☐ **Name** _____
Address _____
_____
☐ Bride   ☐ Groom   ☐ Friend   ☐ Family
Ceremony _____ # Reception _____
Gift _____ ☐ Thank-you sent

☐ ☐ **Name** _____
Address _____
_____
☐ Bride   ☐ Groom   ☐ Friend   ☐ Family
Ceremony _____ # Reception _____
Gift _____ ☐ Thank-you sent

Guests and Gifts

RSVP

Yes **No**

❏ ❏ **Name** _____
Address _____
_____
❏ Bride   ❏ Groom   ❏ Friend   ❏ Family
Ceremony _____ # Reception _____
Gift _____ ❏ Thank-you sent

❏ ❏ **Name** _____
Address _____
_____
❏ Bride   ❏ Groom   ❏ Friend   ❏ Family
Ceremony _____ # Reception _____
Gift _____ ❏ Thank-you sent

❏ ❏ **Name** _____
Address _____
_____
❏ Bride   ❏ Groom   ❏ Friend   ❏ Family
Ceremony _____ # Reception _____
Gift _____ ❏ Thank-you sent

❏ ❏ **Name** _____
Address _____
_____
❏ Bride   ❏ Groom   ❏ Friend   ❏ Family
Ceremony _____ # Reception _____
Gift _____ ❏ Thank-you sent

❏ ❏ **Name** _____
Address _____
_____
❏ Bride   ❏ Groom   ❏ Friend   ❏ Family
Ceremony _____ # Reception _____
Gift _____ ❏ Thank-you sent

Guests and Gifts

RSVP

Yes   No

☐   ☐   **Name** _____

Address _____

_____

☐ Bride   ☐ Groom   ☐ Friend   ☐ Family

\# Ceremony _____   # Reception _____

Gift _____ ☐ Thank-you sent

☐   ☐   **Name** _____

Address _____

_____

☐ Bride   ☐ Groom   ☐ Friend   ☐ Family

\# Ceremony _____   # Reception _____

Gift _____ ☐ Thank-you sent

☐   ☐   **Name** _____

Address _____

_____

☐ Bride   ☐ Groom   ☐ Friend   ☐ Family

\# Ceremony _____   # Reception _____

Gift _____ ☐ Thank-you sent

☐   ☐   **Name** _____

Address _____

_____

☐ Bride   ☐ Groom   ☐ Friend   ☐ Family

\# Ceremony _____   # Reception _____

Gift _____ ☐ Thank-you sent

☐   ☐   **Name** _____

Address _____

_____

☐ Bride   ☐ Groom   ☐ Friend   ☐ Family

\# Ceremony _____   # Reception _____

Gift _____ ☐ Thank-you sent

Guests and Gifts

RSVP

Yes No

☐ ☐ **Name** _____

Address _____

_____

☐ Bride   ☐ Groom   ☐ Friend   ☐ Family

\# Ceremony _____   \# Reception _____

Gift _____ ☐ Thank-you sent

☐ ☐ **Name** _____

Address _____

_____

☐ Bride   ☐ Groom   ☐ Friend   ☐ Family

\# Ceremony _____   \# Reception _____

Gift _____ ☐ Thank-you sent

☐ ☐ **Name** _____

Address _____

_____

☐ Bride   ☐ Groom   ☐ Friend   ☐ Family

\# Ceremony _____   \# Reception _____

Gift _____ ☐ Thank-you sent

☐ ☐ **Name** _____

Address _____

_____

☐ Bride   ☐ Groom   ☐ Friend   ☐ Family

\# Ceremony _____   \# Reception _____

Gift _____ ☐ Thank-you sent

☐ ☐ **Name** _____

Address _____

_____

☐ Bride   ☐ Groom   ☐ Friend   ☐ Family

\# Ceremony _____   \# Reception _____

Gift _____ ☐ Thank-you sent

Guests and Gifts

RSVP

Yes No

❑ ❑ **Name** _____
Address _____
_____
❑ Bride   ❑ Groom   ❑ Friend   ❑ Family
Ceremony _____ # Reception _____
Gift _____ ❑ Thank-you sent

❑ ❑ **Name** _____
Address _____
_____
❑ Bride   ❑ Groom   ❑ Friend   ❑ Family
Ceremony _____ # Reception _____
Gift _____ ❑ Thank-you sent

❑ ❑ **Name** _____
Address _____
_____
❑ Bride   ❑ Groom   ❑ Friend   ❑ Family
Ceremony _____ # Reception _____
Gift _____ ❑ Thank-you sent

❑ ❑ **Name** _____
Address _____
_____
❑ Bride   ❑ Groom   ❑ Friend   ❑ Family
Ceremony _____ # Reception _____
Gift _____ ❑ Thank-you sent

❑ ❑ **Name** _____
Address _____
_____
❑ Bride   ❑ Groom   ❑ Friend   ❑ Family
Ceremony _____ # Reception _____
Gift _____ ❑ Thank-you sent

Guests and Gifts

RSVP

Yes No

❑ ❑ **Name** _____
Address _____
_____
❑ Bride ❑ Groom ❑ Friend ❑ Family
Ceremony _____ # Reception _____
Gift _____ ❑ Thank-you sent

❑ ❑ **Name** _____
Address _____
_____
❑ Bride ❑ Groom ❑ Friend ❑ Family
Ceremony _____ # Reception _____
Gift _____ ❑ Thank-you sent

❑ ❑ **Name** _____
Address _____
_____
❑ Bride ❑ Groom ❑ Friend ❑ Family
Ceremony _____ # Reception _____
Gift _____ ❑ Thank-you sent

❑ ❑ **Name** _____
Address _____
_____
❑ Bride ❑ Groom ❑ Friend ❑ Family
Ceremony _____ # Reception _____
Gift _____ ❑ Thank-you sent

❑ ❑ **Name** _____
Address _____
_____
❑ Bride ❑ Groom ❑ Friend ❑ Family
Ceremony _____ # Reception _____
Gift _____ ❑ Thank-you sent

Guests and Gifts

RSVP

Yes No

☐ ☐ **Name** _____
Address _____
_____
☐ Bride ☐ Groom ☐ Friend ☐ Family
Ceremony _____ # Reception _____
Gift _____ ☐ Thank-you sent

☐ ☐ **Name** _____
Address _____
_____
☐ Bride ☐ Groom ☐ Friend ☐ Family
Ceremony _____ # Reception _____
Gift _____ ☐ Thank-you sent

☐ ☐ **Name** _____
Address _____
_____
☐ Bride ☐ Groom ☐ Friend ☐ Family
Ceremony _____ # Reception _____
Gift _____ ☐ Thank-you sent

☐ ☐ **Name** _____
Address _____
_____
☐ Bride ☐ Groom ☐ Friend ☐ Family
Ceremony _____ # Reception _____
Gift _____ ☐ Thank-you sent

☐ ☐ **Name** _____
Address _____
_____
☐ Bride ☐ Groom ☐ Friend ☐ Family
Ceremony _____ # Reception _____
Gift _____ ☐ Thank-you sent

Guests and Gifts

Yes   No

❑   ❑   **Name** _____
Address _____
_____
❑ Bride   ❑ Groom   ❑ Friend   ❑ Family
Ceremony _____   # Reception _____
Gift _____   ❑ Thank-you sent

❑   ❑   **Name** _____
Address _____
_____
❑ Bride   ❑ Groom   ❑ Friend   ❑ Family
Ceremony _____   # Reception _____
Gift _____   ❑ Thank-you sent

❑   ❑   **Name** _____
Address _____
_____
❑ Bride   ❑ Groom   ❑ Friend   ❑ Family
Ceremony _____   # Reception _____
Gift _____   ❑ Thank-you sent

❑   ❑   **Name** _____
Address _____
_____
❑ Bride   ❑ Groom   ❑ Friend   ❑ Family
Ceremony _____   # Reception _____
Gift _____   ❑ Thank-you sent

❑   ❑   **Name** _____
Address _____
_____
❑ Bride   ❑ Groom   ❑ Friend   ❑ Family
Ceremony _____   # Reception _____
Gift _____   ❑ Thank-you sent

Guests and Gifts

RSVP

Yes **No**
☐ ☐ **Name** _____
Address _____
_____
☐ Bride ☐ Groom ☐ Friend ☐ Family
\# Ceremony _____ \# Reception _____
Gift _____ ☐ Thank-you sent

☐ ☐ **Name** _____
Address _____
_____
☐ Bride ☐ Groom ☐ Friend ☐ Family
\# Ceremony _____ \# Reception _____
Gift _____ ☐ Thank-you sent

☐ ☐ **Name** _____
Address _____
_____
☐ Bride ☐ Groom ☐ Friend ☐ Family
\# Ceremony _____ \# Reception _____
Gift _____ ☐ Thank-you sent

☐ ☐ **Name** _____
Address _____
_____
☐ Bride ☐ Groom ☐ Friend ☐ Family
\# Ceremony _____ \# Reception _____
Gift _____ ☐ Thank-you sent

☐ ☐ **Name** _____
Address _____
_____
☐ Bride ☐ Groom ☐ Friend ☐ Family
\# Ceremony _____ \# Reception _____
Gift _____ ☐ Thank-you sent

Please make duplicate copies if necessary

Gift Registry Checklist

FORMAL DINNERWARE

Store_____
Phone_____
Pattern_____
Manufacturer_____

Description	Need	Rec'd
Bowl: cereal	___	___
Bowl: fruit	___	___
Bowl: serving	___	___
Bowl: soup	___	___
Butter dish	___	___
Coffee pot	___	___
Cup & saucer	___	___
Gravy boat	___	___
Plate: bread & butter	___	___
Plate: dessert/salad	___	___
Plate: dinner	___	___
Platter: small	___	___
Platter: medium	___	___
Platter: large	___	___
Salt/pepper	___	___
Sugar/creamer	___	___
Teapot	___	___
Vegetable dish	___	___

FORMAL STEMWARE

Store_____
Phone_____
Pattern_____
Manufacturer_____

Description	Need	Rec'd
Brandy	___	___
Champagne	___	___
Cocktail	___	___
Cordial	___	___
Goblets	___	___
Iced tea	___	___
Wine	___	___
Other: ____	___	___

FORMAL FLATWARE

Store_____
Phone_____
Pattern_____
Manufacturer_____

Description	Need	Rec'd
Carving set	___	___
Fork: cocktail	___	___
Fork: cold meat	___	___
Fork: dinner	___	___
Fork: salad/dessert	___	___
Fork: serving	___	___
Gravy ladle	___	___
Knife: butter	___	___
Knife: cake	___	___
Knife: dinner	___	___
Knife: steak	___	___
Pie server	___	___
Salad set	___	___
Silver chest	___	___
Spoon: demitasse	___	___
Spoon: iced tea	___	___
Spoon: serving	___	___
Spoon: soup	___	___
Spoon/Tongs: sugar	___	___
Spoon: tablespoon	___	___
Spoon: tea/dessert	___	___

INFORMAL GLASSWARE

Store_____
Phone_____
Pattern_____
Manufacturer_____

Description	Need	Rec'd
Beer mugs	___	___
Cocktail	___	___
Goblets	___	___
Highball	___	___
Iced tea	___	___
Juice	___	___
Old-fashioned	___	___
Wine	___	___

Guests and Gifts

Informal Dinnerware

Store_____

Phone_____

Pattern_____

Manufacturer_____

Description	Need	Rec'd
No. of place settings	_____	_____
Serving pieces	_____	_____
Other:		
_____	_____	_____
_____	_____	_____
_____	_____	_____

Informal Flatware

Store_____

Phone_____

Pattern_____

Manufacturer_____

Description	Need	Rec'd
No. of place settings	_____	_____
Serving pieces	_____	_____
Steak knives	_____	_____
Carving set	_____	_____
Other:		
_____	_____	_____
_____	_____	_____
_____	_____	_____

Kitchen Accessories

Description	Need	Rec'd
Bakeware:		
Bread pan	_____	_____
Cake pan	_____	_____
Casserole dishes	_____	_____
Cookie sheets	_____	_____
Cupcake pan	_____	_____
Lasagna pan	_____	_____
Loaf pan	_____	_____
Pizza pan	_____	_____
Popover	_____	_____
Quiche	_____	_____
Springform	_____	_____
Soufflé	_____	_____
Blender	_____	_____
Canister set	_____	_____

	Need	Rec'd
Can opener (electric)	_____	_____
Coffee grinder	_____	_____
Coffee maker	_____	_____
Colander	_____	_____
Cook books	_____	_____
Cookie jar	_____	_____
Corkscrew	_____	_____
Crockpot	_____	_____
Cutlery	_____	_____
Cutting board	_____	_____
Deep fryer	_____	_____
Electric knife	_____	_____
Electric skillet	_____	_____
Espresso machine	_____	_____
Fondue pot	_____	_____
Food processor	_____	_____
Fry pan: small	_____	_____
Fry pan: large	_____	_____
Grater	_____	_____
Ice bucket	_____	_____
Ice cream scoop	_____	_____
Juicer	_____	_____
Measuring cups	_____	_____
Measuring spoons	_____	_____
Microwave	_____	_____
Microwave cookware	_____	_____
Mitts	_____	_____
Mixer	_____	_____
Mixing bowls	_____	_____
Muffin tins	_____	_____
Omelet pan	_____	_____
Ovenware	_____	_____
Picnic basket	_____	_____
Pressure cooker	_____	_____
Roaster	_____	_____
Salad bowl set	_____	_____
Saucepan: small	_____	_____
Saucepan: medium	_____	_____
Saucepan: large	_____	_____
Smoke detector	_____	_____
Spice rack	_____	_____
Storage containers	_____	_____
Tea kettle	_____	_____
Toaster	_____	_____
Toaster oven	_____	_____
Waffle iron	_____	_____

KITCHEN ACCESSORIES (cont')

Description	Need	Rec'd
Wok	___	___
Wooden salad bowl set	___	___
Other:		
_____	___	___
_____	___	___
_____	___	___

KITCHEN & TABLE LINENS

Description	Need	Rec'd
Aprons	___	___
Dish cloths	___	___
Dish towels	___	___
Napkins: casual	___	___
Napkins: formal	___	___
Napkin rings: casual	___	___
Napkin rings: formal	___	___
Placemats	___	___
Pot holders	___	___
Tablecloths: casual	___	___
Tablecloths: formal	___	___
Other:		
_____	___	___
_____	___	___

BATH LINENS & ACCESSORIES

Description	Need	Rec'd
Bath mat	___	___
Bath rug	___	___
Bath towels	___	___
Beach towels	___	___
Fingertip holder	___	___
Fingertip towels	___	___
Guest towels	___	___
Hamper	___	___
Hand towels	___	___
Scale	___	___
Shower curtain	___	___
Soap dish	___	___
Tissue cover	___	___
Toothbrush holder	___	___
Towel stand	___	___

	Need	Rec'd
Washcloths	___	___
Wastebasket	___	___
Other:		
_____	___	___
_____	___	___
_____	___	___

BED LINENS

Description	Need	Rec'd
Bedspread	___	___
Blankets: thermal	___	___
Blankets: conventional	___	___
Blankets: electric	___	___
Comforter: down	___	___
Comforter: conventional	___	___
Duvet cover	___	___
Mattress pad	___	___
Pillowcases	___	___
Pillows: down	___	___
Pillows: synthetic	___	___
Shams	___	___
Sheets: fitted	___	___
Sheets: flat	___	___
Sheets: flannel	___	___
Sheets: waterbed	___	___
Other:		
_____	___	___
_____	___	___
_____	___	___

ELECTRONICS

Description	Need	Rec'd
CD player	___	___
CD storage unit	___	___
Calculator	___	___
Camera	___	___
Camera equipment	___	___
Clock radio	___	___
Computer	___	___
Security devices	___	___
Stereo	___	___
Telephone	___	___
Telephone: portable	___	___
Telephone: cellular	___	___

ELECTRONICS (cont')

Description	Need	Rec'd
Television	——	——
Typewriter	——	——
Video camera	——	——
Videotape player	——	——
Video storage unit	——	——
Other:		
_____	——	——
_____	——	——
_____	——	——

HOUSEWARES

Description	Need	Rec'd
Barbecue	——	——
Broom	——	——
Clock: kitchen	——	——
Dustpan	——	——
Fireplace equipment	——	——
Garbage pail	——	——
Iron	——	——
Ironing board	——	——
Mop	——	——
Smoke alarms	——	——
Stepstool	——	——
Tool kit	——	——
Vacuum cleaner	——	——
Wastebaskets	——	——
Other:		
_____	——	——
_____	——	——
_____	——	——

DECORATIVE ITEMS

Description	Need	Rec'd
Area rugs	——	——
Art	——	——
Baskets	——	——

	Need	Rec'd
Bookends	——	——
Clocks	——	——
Lamps	——	——
Vases	——	——
Other:		
_____	——	——
_____	——	——
_____	——	——

MISCELLANEOUS

Description	Need	Rec'd
Bar accessories	——	——
Bicycles	——	——
Camping gear:		
Sleeping bags	——	——
Tent	——	——
Card table & chairs	——	——
Desk	——	——
Exercise equipment	——	——
Linen storage	——	——
Luggage:		
Carry-on	——	——
Garment bag	——	——
Overnight	——	——
Pullman	——	——
Travel kit	——	——
Magazine rack	——	——
Patio furniture	——	——
Plants	——	——
Planters	——	——
Sewing machine	——	——
Shoe rack	——	——
Sporting equipment	——	——
TV tables	——	——
Tools	——	——
Other:		
_____	——	——
_____	——	——

Out-of-Town Guests Checklist ——————————

Due Date | To Do

❑ _____ Design and print maps, with directions, to the wedding and reception sites.

❑ _____ Enclose a copy of map in the out-of-town guests invitation packet.

❑ _____ Fill out the *Wedding Week Itinerary* page. List parties, outings and events to be held the week before the wedding. Include a copy in the out-of-town guests invitation packet.

❑ _____ Make the following arrangements for your out-of-town guests:
  ❑ Travel: coordinate their arrival dates and times and who is to pick them up at the airport.
  ❑ Accommodations: contact hotels for room rates and availability.
  ❑ Transportation: contact rental car companies for special weekend rates and ask for maps of your area.

❑ _____ Ask friends and family members if they are able to offer special accommodations for any out-of-town guests and attendants.

❑ _____ Order or make your own gift baskets for the out-of-town guests.

❑ _____ Place gift baskets in hotel rooms.

NOTES

_____

_____

_____

_____

_____

_____

_____

_____

_____

Guests and Gifts

Accomodations for Out-of-Town Guests ——————

❑ Hotel ❑ Motel ❑ Bed & Breakfast ❑ Private home

❑ Other _____

Location _____

Address _____

Phone _____ Contact _____ ❑ Confirmed

Prices _____

Description _____

Guests staying here _____

_____

❑ Hotel ❑ Motel ❑ Bed & Breakfast ❑ Private home
❑ Other _____

Location _____

Address _____

Phone _____ Contact _____ ❑ Confirmed

Prices _____

Description _____

Guests staying here _____

_____

❑ Hotel ❑ Motel ❑ Bed & Breakfast ❑ Private home
❑ Other _____

Location _____

Address _____

Phone _____ Contact _____ ❑ Confirmed

Prices _____

Description _____

Guests staying here _____

_____

Please make duplicate copies if necessary

Guests and Gifts

Out-of-Town Guests

Name _____ Phone _____
Arrival date / time _____ Departure date / time_____
Accommodation needs _____ Transportation needs _____

Name _____ Phone _____
Arrival date / time _____ Departure date / time _____
Accommodation needs _____ Transportation needs _____

Name _____ Phone _____
Arrival date / time _____ Departure date / time_____
Accommodation needs _____ Transportation needs _____

Name _____ Phone _____
Arrival date / time _____ Departure date / time_____
Accommodation needs _____ Transportation needs _____

Name _____ Phone _____
Arrival date / time _____ Departure date / time_____
Accommodation needs _____ Transportation needs _____

Name _____ Phone _____
Arrival date / time _____ Departure date / time_____
Accommodation needs _____ Transportation needs _____

Name _____ Phone _____
Arrival date / time _____ Departure date / time_____
Accommodation needs _____ Transportation needs _____

Name _____ Phone _____
Arrival date / time _____ Departure date / time_____
Accommodation needs _____ Transportation needs _____

Guests and Gifts

Out-of-Town Guests

Name _____ Phone _____
Arrival date / time _____ Departure date / time_____
Accommodation needs _____ Transportation needs _____

Name _____ Phone _____
Arrival date / time _____ Departure date / time _____
Accommodation needs _____ Transportation needs_____

Name _____ Phone _____
Arrival date / time _____ Departure date / time_____
Accommodation needs _____ Transportation needs_____

Name _____ Phone _____
Arrival date / time _____ Departure date / time_____
Accommodation needs _____ Transportation needs_____

Name _____ Phone _____
Arrival date / time _____ Departure date / time_____
Accommodation needs _____ Transportation needs_____

Name _____ Phone _____
Arrival date / time _____ Departure date / time_____
Accommodation needs _____ Transportation needs_____

Name _____ Phone _____
Arrival date / time _____ Departure date / time_____
Accommodation needs _____ Transportation needs_____

Name _____ Phone _____
Arrival date / time _____ Departure date / time_____
Accommodation needs _____ Transportation needs_____

Please make duplicate copies if necessary

Planning the Ceremony

Ceremony Planning Tips

RESERVING THE CEREMONY SITE

As soon as the wedding date and budget are set, start searching for a wedding location. The date of your wedding may depend on the availability of the ceremony site. Keep in mind that prime dates and locations can book up to a year in advance. You will also need to determine the number of guests and the type of wedding you want before reserving a site.

If you are looking for a unique location, ask friends and family members for referrals. Also, ask wedding professionals for their recommendations. Use the *Wedding Vendors Referral Form* (page 63-64) to keep track of and follow up with referrals.

Select and reserve your ceremony site as soon as possible. Use the *Selecting a Ceremony Site* (page 135) form to help ensure the best decision.

Once you have selected a ceremony site, get everything in writing and sign a contract! Pay the smallest deposit you can and pay with a credit card. Use the *Ceremony Site Worksheet* (page 137-39) as a letter of agreement. This worksheet describes the products and services your wedding site provides.

THE CEREMONY SITE

Ask if a wedding is booked before or after yours. This will let you know how much time you have for decorating, wedding photos and the receiving line.

Planning the Ceremony

Before renting any items, find out what accessories the wedding site will provide: the aisle runner, candelabra, kneeling bench, etc. (See: *Ceremony Supply List*, page 142.)

Inquire about restrictions regarding music, candles, decorations, photography and videography, and tossing of rice, birdseed, flower petals or bubbles.

Find out if the ceremony site has adequate space for the bridal party to dress. If there are no dressing rooms, decide where and when the bridal party will dress. Allow at least two hours to dress.

If you are having an outdoor wedding, make arrangements for an alternate location in the event of bad weather.

THE CEREMONY REHEARSAL

Set the date and time of the rehearsal with your officiant at the same time you arrange for his or her services for your wedding. The rehearsal is usually held the evening before the wedding. Invite everyone involved with the ceremony to the rehearsal. This is your opportunity to run through the ceremony proceedings with your officiant, the wedding party, the musicians and your parents in attendance. (See: *Rehearsal Dinner Worksheet*, page 81.)

THE SERVICE

Once the location has been booked, begin meeting with your officiant to discuss the wedding service and find out about any rules they might have. You will want to know what their standard service consists of and if you can personalize it, or even write your own vows. (See: *Bride's Vows and Groom's Vows*, page 141.)

Consider having a wedding program. It provides the names of the wedding participants and helps your guests follow the ceremony.

THE GUEST REGISTER

The guest register can be placed at either the ceremony or the reception site.

Display your guest register, along with an elegant pen and pen holder, on a decorated table in a foyer, or at the entry to the ceremony. Have an extra pen available in case it runs out of ink. If you are expecting a lot of guests, consider having two guest registers. Coordinate the placement and decorating of the table with your ceremony site director.

Planning the Ceremony

Your guest register attendant should arrive before the guests to make sure the table is decorated and where it should be, and that the register and pen are on the table. The attendant is responsible for inviting your guests to sign in. They also need to remove the guest register and either take it to the reception site or give it to someone for safekeeping.

Ceremony Site Ideas

❑ Private Home
❑ Resort
❑ Private Club
❑ College Chapels
❑ Wineries
❑ Museum
❑ Beach

❑ Hotel
❑ Restaurant
❑ City Hall
❑ Cruise Boat
❑ Art Galleries
❑ Theater
❑ Mountains

❑ Church or Synagogue
❑ Gardens or Parks
❑ Banquet Room/Catering Hall
❑ Bed and Breakfast Inn
❑ Historic Building
❑ Theme Park
❑ Hot-air Balloon

Ceremony Theme Ideas

❑ Victorian
❑ Christmas
❑ Gay Nineties
❑ Modern

❑ Country
❑ Valentine's Day
❑ Royal Elegance
❑ The Fifties

❑ Old-Fashioned
❑ Flower Garden
❑ Romantic Candlelight
❑ Hollywood Movies Theme

Ceremony Ideas

Use this page to write down ideas for your ceremony including the style, theme, decorations, color scheme, etc.

Wedding Style: ❑ Very Formal   ❑ Formal   ❑ Semi-Formal   ❑ Informal

_____

_____

_____

_____

_____

_____

_____

_____

_____

Ceremony Checklist

Due Date	To Do
❑ _____	Reserve the ceremony site.
❑ _____	Sign agreements and pay deposits.
❑ _____	Get the marriage license.
❑ _____	Ask about any restrictions the site has: decorations, music, photography/videography, tossing of rice, birdseed or flower petals, or blowing of bubbles.
❑ _____	Select the members of your wedding party. (See: *The Wedding Party*)
❑ _____	Make arrangements for a dressing location for the bridal party.
❑ _____	Book the officiant. (See: *Officiant Information*)
❑ _____	Plan the ceremony with the officiant.
❑ _____	Place officiant's fee in a sealed envelope for delivery by the best man.
❑ _____	Hire wedding professionals: ❑ Ceremony coordinator ❑ Vocalist and organist/musicians ❑ Photographer/videographer ❑ Transportation ❑ Florist
❑ _____	Be sure the photographer/videographer has a list of poses/events you want photographed/videotaped. (See: *Photo and Video Checklist*)
❑ _____	Select wedding music. (See: *Ceremony Music Selections*)
❑ _____	Choose the decorations.
❑ _____	Purchase or rent decorations/items you will need for the ceremony. (See: *Ceremony Supply List*)
❑ _____	Recruit volunteers to help with duties. (See: *List of Ceremony Helpers*)
❑ _____	Fill out the Ceremony Timetable form and make a copy for the ceremony coordinator.
❑ _____	Check your supply list, gather and pack items. (See: *Wedding Day Supply Checklist*)
❑ _____	Confirm major ceremony details one month before the wedding.
❑ _____	Confirm all ceremony details two weeks before the wedding.

Selecting a Ceremony Site

Estimate #1

Appointment date _____ Time _____

Business _____

Address _____

Contact_____ Phone _____

Ceremony site budget $ _____

Estimated total cost $ _____

Deposit required $_____

Cancellation policy _____

❏ Viewed site where ceremony would be held.
❏ Picked up price list and brochure.

Type of Location
❏ Church ❏ Chapel ❏ Hotel
❏ Country Club ❏ Park/Garden ❏ Other

QUESTIONS TO ASK

What dates are available? _____

What times are available?_____

Would there be a wedding held before or after mine?

What is the religious denomination?_____

Do vows need to be approved? _____

Minimum/maximum # of guests allowed?_____

What is the room size and decor? _____

Are there dressing rooms for the wedding party? ___

Is it handicapped-accessible? _____

What are your parking facilities? _____

Do you provide any of the following?

❏ Officiant ❏ Altar

❏ Ceremony coordinator ❏ Kneeling cushion

❏ An organist ❏ Guest register table

❏ Aisle runner ❏ Other _____

Are there any restrictions for the following?

Service _____

Music _____

Candles _____

Decorations _____

Photography _____

Videography _____

Tossing of rice, birdseed, flower petals or bubbles ____

Other _____

PRICES

Site rental fee _____

Clergy fee _____

Wedding director's fee _____

Organist's fee _____

Janitor's fee _____

Parking fee/valet service fee _____

SITE DESCRIPTION

_____

_____

Please make duplicate copies if necessary

Selecting a Ceremony Site —————————————

Estimate #2

Appointment date _____ Time _____

Business _____

Address _____

Contact_____ Phone _____

Ceremony site budget $ _____

Estimated total cost $ _____

Deposit required $_____

Cancellation policy _____

❑ Viewed site where ceremony would be held.
❑ Picked up price list and brochure.

Type of Location
❑ Church ❑ Chapel ❑ Hotel
❑ Country Club ❑ Park/Garden ❑ Other

QUESTIONS TO ASK

What dates are available? _____

What times are available?_____

Would there be a wedding held before or after mine?

What is the religious denomination?_____

Do vows need to be approved? _____

Minimum/maximum # of guests allowed?_____

What is the room size and decor? _____

Are there dressing rooms for the wedding party? ____

Is it handicapped-accessible? _____

What are your parking facilities? _____

Do you provide any of the following?
❑ Officiant ❑ Altar
❑ Ceremony coordinator ❑ Kneeling cushion
❑ An organist ❑ Guest register table
❑ Aisle runner ❑ Other _____

Are there any restrictions for the following?

Service _____

Music _____

Candles _____

Decorations _____

Photography _____

Videography _____

Tossing of rice, birdseed, flower petals or bubbles _____

Other _____

PRICES

Site rental fee _____

Clergy fee _____

Wedding director's fee _____

Organist's fee _____

Janitor's fee _____

Parking fee/valet service fee _____

SITE DESCRIPTION

_____

_____

Please make duplicate copies if necessary

Ceremony Site Worksheet ————————————————

Location _____

Address_____

Phone _____ Contact _____ ❑ Confirmed

Wedding day coordinator _____ Phone _____

Officiant_____ Phone _____

Date Reserved _____

Time: Set-up _____ Start _____ End _____

Rehearsal Date _____ Rehearsal time _____

Number of Guests: Invited _____ Confirmed _____

Attendants: Number of bridesmaids _____ Number of groomsmen/ushers _____

❑ Flower Girl ❑ Ring Bearer ❑ Other _____

Dressing Rooms

Number available _____ Capacity _____

If there are no dressing rooms at the ceremony site, list where and when the bridal party will dress for the wedding:

	Dressing Location	**Time to Get Dressed**
Bride	_____	_____
Maid of honor	_____	_____
Bridesmaids	_____	_____
Groom	_____	_____
Best man	_____	_____
Groomsmen/Ushers	_____	_____

Planning the Ceremony

Site Setup	Setup Time	Notes
❑ Decorations	_____	_____
❑ Gift table	_____	_____
❑ Guest register table	_____	_____
❑ Musicians	_____	_____
❑ Vocalist	_____	_____
❑ Photographer	_____	_____
❑ Videographer	_____	_____
❑ Chairs	_____	_____
❑ Tent	_____	_____
❑ _____	_____	_____
❑ _____	_____	_____
❑ _____	_____	_____
❑ _____	_____	_____

Restrictions

❑ Candles _____

❑ Decorations _____

❑ Music _____

❑ Photography _____

❑ Rice, flower petals, birdseed, bubbles _____

❑ Videography _____

❑ Wedding vows _____

❑ _____ _____

❑ _____ _____

❑ _____ _____

❑ _____ _____

COST

Budget_____ Actual _____

Paid by: ❑ Credit Card ❑ Check ❑ Cash

Site fee: Per hour_____ Number of hours _____ Flat fee _____

Officiant's fee_____ Music_____ Janitor_____

Deposit _____ Date due_____ ❑ Deposit paid

Balance _____ Date due_____ ❑ Balance paid

Cancellation policy _____

_____   _____
Service Representative Signature   Date

_____   _____
Bridal Party Signature   Date

Use this worksheet as an agreement form and have the service representative sign and date it.

Planning the Ceremony

Officiant Information ─────────────────────────

Name _____

Address _____

Phone _____ Contact _____ ❏ Confirmed

Denomination _____

Officiant's fee _____

Wedding date _____ Officiant's arrival time _____

Rehearsal date _____ Rehearsal time _____

Location _____

Special classes

Dates and times _____

Location _____

Checklist

❏ _____ Book officiant at least six months in advance.

❏ _____ Schedule the rehearsal with officiant before booking the rehearsal dinner.

❏ _____ Invite the officiant and their spouse or guest to the rehearsal dinner.

❏ _____ Discuss with the officiant your plans for music (some do not allow secular music to be played during the ceremony).

❏ _____ Discuss photography/videograph (some do not allow flashes and filming during the ceremony).

❏ _____ Arrange for the best man to give an envelope with the fee in it to the officiant in private after the service and before the reception.

❏ _____ Be sure to invite the officiant and their guest to the reception. If they attend, they are usually seated at the parents' table.

❏ _____ _____

❏ _____ _____

❏ _____ _____

Bride's Vows

_____
_____
_____
_____
_____
_____
_____
_____
_____
_____
_____
_____
_____

Groom's Vows

_____
_____
_____
_____
_____
_____
_____
_____
_____
_____
_____
_____
_____
_____

Planning the Ceremony

Ceremony Supply List

Item	Source/Description	Qty	Cost	Total
Guest register table				
Gift table				
Aisle candelabra				
Altar candelabra				
Floor candelabra				
Candlelighters				
Candles				
Flower stands				
Aisle stanchions				
Aisle runner				
Altar				
Arch				
Canopy				
Chairs				
Kneeling bench				
Coat/hat rack				
Lighting				
Microphone				
Audio equipment				
Tents				
Umbrellas				
Fans				
Heaters				
Bubbles, rice, birdseed, flower petals to toss				

TOTAL SUPPLY EXPENSES $ _____

List of Ceremony Helpers —————————————

Duties	Person Responsible
Ceremony coordinator	
Set-up helper(s)	
Decoration helper(s)	
Photographer's assistant	
Videographer's assistant	
Bring marriage license	
Bring wedding rings	
Bring ring bearer pillow	
Take boutonnieres to ushers, fathers, grandfathers and helpers	
Take corsages to mothers, helpers and grandmothers	
Take flower bouquets to bride and her attendants	
Head usher	
Pass out wedding programs	
Guest register attendant	
Gift attendant	
Pass out rice, flowers, birdseed, etc.	
Give fee to officiant	
Give fee to musician/soloist	
Watch over or lockup dressing room(s) during the ceremony	
Take bride's personal belongings to the reception after the ceremony	
Take wedding gifts from ceremony to the reception	
Cleanup	
Lockup ceremony site	
Return rental equipment	

Ceremony Timetable ——————————————————

Time	Activity
_____	Wake up
_____	Beauty appointments for bridal party
_____	Start to get dressed
_____	Groom and his attendants get ready
_____	Transportation to ceremony site arrives
_____	Depart to ceremony
_____	Ceremony coordinator arrives at ceremony site
_____	Helpers arrive
_____	Florist arrives and decorating begins
_____	Guest register table setup with book and pen
_____	Musicians arrival and setup
_____	Photographer arrives and sets up
_____	Videographer arrives and sets up
_____	Pre-wedding photos taken
_____	Setup and decorating is completed
_____	Ushers arrive (half an hour before the ceremony)
_____	Officiant arrives
_____	Groom and the best man arrive
_____	Music starts
_____	Guests start arriving
_____	Bride, her father and attendants arrive
_____	Guests are all seated
_____	Seat the groom's parents
_____	Seat the bride's mother
_____	Unroll the aisle runner (if applicable)
_____	The groom and groomsmen take their place
_____	Processional begins
_____	Ceremony begins
_____	Recessional begins
_____	Ceremony over
_____	Photo session begins
_____	Transportation arrives for wedding party
_____	Wedding party leaves for reception

Planning the Reception

Reception Planning Tips

RESERVING THE RECEPTION SITE

As soon as the wedding date and budget are set, start searching for a reception location. Keep in mind that prime dates and locations can book up to a year in advance. You will also need to determine the number of guests and the type of reception you want before reserving a site.

Ask friends and family members for referrals to reception sites. Also, ask other wedding professionals for their recommendations. Use the *Wedding Vendors Referral Form* (page 63–64) to keep track of and follow up with referrals.

Select and reserve your reception site as soon as possible. Use the *Selecting a Reception Site* (page 151–52) form to help ensure the best decision.

If you are having an outdoor reception, make arrangements for an alternate location in the event of bad weather.

Once you have selected a reception site, get everything in writing and sign a contract! Pay the smallest deposit you can and pay with a credit card. Use the *Reception Site Worksheet* (page 153–55) as a letter of agreement. This worksheet describes the products and services your reception site provides.

THE RECEPTION

Ask if a reception is booked before or after yours. This will let you know how much time you have for setting up, decorating and cleaning up afterwards.

Before renting any items, find out what the reception site provides. (See *Reception Supply List*, page 173–74.)

Inquire about restrictions regarding music, dancing, candles, decorations, liquor beverages, and tossing of rice, birdseed, flower petals or bubbles.

If your reception site does not provide a coordinator, delegate this responsibility to someone. They need to oversee the event details, greet your guests as they arrive and make sure the reception is running smoothly.

Consider placing disposable wedding cameras on each table; it lets your guests capture the candid moments your photographer might miss. Have someone pick up the cameras after the reception. Be sure to include the cost of developing the film in your budget.

Go over the *Reception Announcements* form with the Master of Ceremonies one month before the wedding. Give your emcee a copy of this form which lists the events to announce and the time to do so.

THE CATERER/MENU

Interview a variety of caterers. Ask to view their portfolios and sample the food. If you are having the reception at a hotel, restaurant or private club, you may be required to use their caterer.

Find out what services the caterer provides. Some only do food preparation and serving. Others may provide the wedding cake, rental equipment, bartending services, floral decorations, cleanup, etc.

Ask the reception site manager if they will allow you to bring in your own caterer and if your caterer can use the kitchen facilities.

You should serve a meal appropriate to the time you are holding your reception. Work with your caterer or banquet manager to select an appropriate menu.

Breakfast: before 11:00 A.M.
Brunch/Luncheon: 11:00 A.M. – 1:00 P.M.
Hors d'Oeuvres or Cake and Punch: 1:00 P.M. – 4:00 P.M.
Dinner: 4:00 P.M. – 7:00 P.M.
Hors d'Oeuvres or Cake and Punch: 7:00 P.M. –

If you are serving buffet style, make sure they set the plates at the beginning of the table and silverware and napkins at the end.

Most caterers charge on a per-person basis. Be sure to figure in the beverages, tax, tip and any added charges to determine the total per-person catering price.

A no-host or "cash" bar means your guests pay for their own drinks. If you have an open bar, the drinks are paid for by the person hosting the reception. If an open bar is not in your budget, serve just champagne, wine and soft drinks.

Usually one week before the reception, the caterer will ask you to guarantee a certain number of guests and you will be billed for that number. If extra guests show up, you will probably be billed for them. Ask your caterer about their policies.

SEATING ARRANGEMENTS

Traditionally, for a sit-down meal, the wedding party sits at a head table. The table can be any shape and is sometimes elevated so everyone can see the wedding party. The bride and groom sit in the center, the groom is on the bride's left, with the maid of honor next to him. The best man sits on the bride's right. The rest of the ushers and bridesmaids are alternately seated on either side.

The parents of the bride and groom, the wedding officiant and grandparents are usually seated at a table located near the head table. You may want one table for the bride's family and one for the groom's family.

THE RECEIVING LINE

The receiving line is the first element of the reception, unless you had one after the ceremony. In deciding the lineup for the receiving line, there is no "right" way to do it. The line can be formed as follows:

The mother of the bride with the father of the bride, followed by the groom's mother and father, and then the bride and the groom.

The bride's mother with the groom's father, the bride and the groom, and the groom's mother.

The bride's mother with the groom's father, the bride and the groom, the groom's mother, the maid of honor, and the bridesmaids.

The bride's mother with the groom's father, the bride and the groom, the groom's mother with the bride's father, the maid of honor, and the bridesmaids.

The bride's mother with the groom's father, the groom's mother with the bride's father, the bride and the groom, and the maid of honor.

Planning the Reception

The bride's mother first, the groom's mother and father, the bride and the groom, and the maid of honor with the best man.

Divorced parents should not stand together in the receiving line.

Traditionally, the bride's father sponsors the reception and is the host of the occasion. He does not stand in the receiving line, but mingles with the guests and makes sure everything is running smoothly.

If more guests are invited to the ceremony than to the reception, consider having the receiving line immediately after the ceremony, outside the entrance.

Arrange to have the receiving line in a location that does not require guests to crowd into a small space. Traffic should flow easily from the end of the receiving line into the reception.

When you are in the receiving line, welcome and thank each guest for coming to your wedding, then introduce them to the person standing next to you. Keep conversations brief; remember, your guests are waiting for you. Be sure to offer refreshments to those waiting.

Our receiving line:

First person _____	6th _____
2nd _____	7th _____
3rd _____	8th _____
4th _____	9th _____
5th _____	10th _____

THE GIFT TABLE

The gift attendant is in charge of your gifts at the reception. Ask them to make sure cards are securely attached to the gifts. They should have Scotch tape with them in case of any loose cards. When the gift is a card, they should mark it "card only." Have someone take the gifts home or to your hotel room after the reception.

GUEST MEMENTOS/PARTY FAVORS

It is a tradition to give your guests a small item as a memento of your wedding. Popular party favors include: candy-coated almonds in netting wrapped with a colored ribbon, personalized matches, personalized napkins, personalized box of mints, personalized box of toothpicks, truffles, and chocolate roses.

TOASTS TO THE NEWLYWEDS

The best man traditionally gives the wedding toast just before the meal is served. The guests should be seated and served something to toast with.

THE FIRST DANCE

The bride and groom's first dance takes place after the meal is served. Before the first song ends, the Master of Ceremonies should instruct the rest of the wedding party to join in with their respective partners. Sometime during the celebration, the bride dances with her father while the groom dances with his mother. The bride and groom should also dance with their new in-laws and their honor attendants.

CAKE-CUTTING CEREMONY

See: *The Wedding Cake* (pages 162–64).

TOSSING THE BOUQUET AND GARTER

These events usually happen toward the end of the reception, or after the cake-cutting ceremony.

The Master of Ceremonies asks all eligible ladies to gather together for the bouquet toss. The bride turns her back to the crowd and tosses the bouquet over her head. It is said that the person catching the bouquet will be the next to marry. Consider having two bouquets. Use a smaller, less expensive one specifically made for tossing so that the wedding bouquet can be preserved.

The Master of Ceremonies then asks all eligible men to gather together for the garter toss. The groom should bring a chair out for the bride to sit on. He removes the garter from the bride's leg, turns his back to the crowd and tosses the garter. It is said that the man who catches the garter will be the next to marry.

THE NEWLYWEDS' GRAND EXIT

Traditionally the bride and groom leave after the bouquet and garter toss. Today, however, it is acceptable for you to stay and dance and mingle with your guests. If you are leaving early, you may want to change into a going-away outfit (check with the reception site about dressing rooms).

TOSSING RICE

Traditionally, rice is tossed over the bride and groom after they leave the ceremony or the reception. Other popular items to use include birdseed, flower petals, confetti or blowing bubbles. Check with your site directors about any restrictions. Have someone hand these out to your guests as you are changing into your going-away outfit.

Reception Checklist

Due Date	To Do

☐ _____ Reserve the reception site.

☐ _____ Sign agreements and pay deposits.

☐ _____ Ask about any restrictions the site has: decorations, liquor, music, tossing of rice, birdseed or flower petals, or blowing of bubbles.

☐ _____ Decide on the reception style, theme and decorations.

☐ _____ Purchase or rent decorations/items you will need for the reception. (See: *Reception Supply List*)

☐ _____ Hire a caterer if the facility doesn't provide catering.

☐ _____ Plan the menu.

☐ _____ Order the wedding cake if the facility or caterer doesn't provide one.

☐ _____ Hire wedding professionals:
- ☐ Reception coordinator
- ☐ Band, DJ or musicians
- ☐ Photographer and/or videographer
- ☐ Caterer
- ☐ Bakery
- ☐ Master of Ceremonies
- ☐ Florist/decoration coordinator
- ☐ Rental company
- ☐ Transportation company

☐ _____ Be sure the photographer/videographer has a list of poses/events you want photographed/videotaped. (See: *Photo and Video Checklist*)

☐ _____ Fill in the *Reception Announcements* form and give a copy to the emcee.

☐ _____ Recruit a volunteer to be the guest register attendant.

☐ _____ Recruit volunteers to help with duties. (See: *List of Reception Helpers*)

☐ _____ Fill out the *Reception Timetable* form and give a copy to the reception coordinator.

☐ _____ Check your supply list, gather and pack items. (See: *Wedding Day Supply Checklist*)

☐ _____ Confirm major reception details one month before your wedding.

☐ _____ Confirm all reception details two weeks before your wedding.

Selecting a Reception Site

Appointment date _____ Time _____

Business _____

Address _____

Contact _____ Phone _____

My budget for the reception site $ _____

Estimated total cost $ _____

Deposit required _____ Cancellation policy _____

❑ Viewed site where reception will be held.

❑ Picked up price list and brochure.

Type of Location

❑ Church hall ❑ Chapel hall ❑ Hotel ❑ Country club ❑ Park/Garden

❑ Other _____

Questions to Ask

What dates are available? _____

What times are available? _____

Would there be a reception held before or after mine? _____

What is the minimum/maximum number of guests allowed? _____

What is the room size and decor? _____

Do you have a fully equipped kitchen? _____

Do you have an in-house caterer? _____

Can we bring in our own caterer? _____

Can our caterer use the kitchen facilities? _____

Do you have changing rooms? _____

Is it handicapped-accessible? _____

What are your parking facilities? _____

What are the cleanup requirements? _____

What about security? _____

Are there any restrictions for the following?

❑ Beverages _____

❑ Dancing _____

Please make duplicate copies if necessary

Planning the Reception

- ❏ Music _____
- ❏ Candles _____
- ❏ Decorations _____
- ❏ Photography _____
- ❏ Videography _____
- ❏ Tossing of rice, birdseed, flower petals or bubbles _____
- ❏ Other _____

Do you provide any of the following?

- ❏ Cake table _____
- ❏ Gift table _____
- ❏ Guest register table _____
- ❏ Dance floor _____
- ❏ Staging _____
- ❏ Sound system _____
- ❏ Microphones _____
- ❏ Audio-visual equipment _____
- ❏ Piano _____
- ❏ Other musical instruments _____
- ❏ Trash cans _____
- ❏ If outdoors: tents, lights, heaters, fans, power outlets, bug
  eliminator: _____
- ❏ Other _____

Prices

Site rental fee _____

Overtime rate _____

Janitor's fee _____

Parking fee/valet service fee _____

Site Description

_____

_____

_____

Please make duplicate copies if necessary

Reception Site Worksheet —————————————————

Location _____

Address_____

Phone _____ Contact _____ ❑ Confirmed

Reception Date _____ Time: from _____ to _____

Setup time_____ Room reserved _____

Occupancy _____ Number of guests invited _____

Date to give final guest count_____ Number confirmed _____

Type of Reception

❑ Cake and Punch   ❑ Hors d'oeuvres   ❑ Buffet   ❑ Sit-down

❑ Open bar /open from _____to_____

❑ Cash bar /open from _____to_____

❑ Renting room only   ❑ Using in-house caterer

❑ Bringing in outside caterer

Services Included

❑ Bartenders
❑ Catering
❑ Cleanup
❑ Security
❑ Setup
❑ Valet parking
❑ Waiters

Equipment Included

❑ Barware
❑ Chairs
❑ Dance floor
❑ Gift table
❑ Guest register table
❑ Tables
❑ Tableware
❑ Linens

Ask About:

❑ Decoration restrictions _____

❑ Dance floor capacity _____

❑ Electrical outlets _____

❑ Insurance _____

❑ Kitchen facilities _____

Planning the Reception

☐ Liquor restrictions _____

☐ Liquor liability _____

☐ Parking facilities _____

☐ Restroom facilities_____

☐ Security _____

☐ Tossing of birdseed, rice, flower petals or blowing of bubbles _____

Room Setup	Setup Time	Person Responsible
☐ Audio-visual	_____	_____
☐ Bar	_____	_____
☐ Cake table	_____	_____
☐ Cake	_____	_____
☐ Cake knife and server	_____	_____
☐ Caterer	_____	_____
☐ Dance floor	_____	_____
☐ Decorations	_____	_____
☐ Gift table	_____	_____
☐ Guest register table	_____	_____
☐ Musicians / DJ	_____	_____
☐ Photographer	_____	_____
☐ Videographer	_____	_____
☐ Place settings	_____	_____
☐ Tables and chairs	_____	_____
☐ Table centerpieces	_____	_____
☐ Tent	_____	_____
☐ _____	_____	_____
☐ _____	_____	_____
☐ _____	_____	_____

Planning the Reception

COST

Budget _____ Actual _____

Paid by: ❑ Credit Card   ❑ Check   ❑ Cash

Room rate _____ ❑ Room fee waived for using in-house caterer

Bartenders/Servers_____ Parking/Valet_____

Cost per-person _____ Tax_____ Gratuity_____

Open bar estimated cost _____ Cash bar charges _____

Deposit_____ Date due _____ ❑ Deposit paid

Balance_____ Date due _____ ❑ Balance paid

Cancellation policy _____

_____   _____

Service Representative Signature   Date

_____   _____

Bridal Party Signature   Date

Use this worksheet as an agreement form and have the service representative sign and date it.

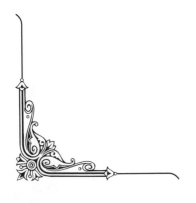

Reception Catering Worksheet ───────────────

Caterer _____

Address_____

Phone _____ Contact _____ ❑ Confirmed

Type of Reception

❑ Cake and punch   ❑ Hors d'oeuvres   ❑ Buffet   ❑ Sit-down
❑ Open bar   ❑ Cash bar   ❑ Wine   ❑ Champagne   ❑ Cocktails
❑ Soft drinks

Reception date_____ Time: from _____ to _____

Setup time _____ Room reserved _____

Occupancy_____ Number of guests invited _____

Date to give final guest count_____ Number confirmed_____

Service

Time food will be set out _____Time food will be taken away _____

Number of bartenders and servers _____

Who assumes liquor liability?_____

If buffet, will bridal party be served?_____

Servers' attire _____

Cleanup _____

Equipment Provided: (tables, chairs, linens, table settings, decorations, etc.)

_____

_____

_____

_____

_____

_____

Planning the Reception

Cost

Budget_____ Actual _____

Paid by: ❏ Credit Card   ❏ Check   ❏ Cash

Room rate _____ ❏ Room fee waived for using in-house caterer

Bartenders/Servers _____ Parking/Valet_____

Cost per-person_____ Tax _____ Gratuity _____

Open bar estimated cost _____ Cash bar charges _____

Deposit _____ Date due _____ ❏ Deposit paid

Balance_____ Date due _____ ❏ Balance paid

Cancellation policy _____

_____   _____
Service Representative Signature   Date

_____   _____
Bridal Party Signature   Date

Use this worksheet as an agreement form and have the service representative sign and date it.

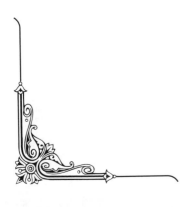

Reception Menu

Hors d'oeuvres
_____
_____
_____

Appetizers
_____
_____
_____

Soup/Salad
_____
_____
_____

Main course
_____
_____
_____

Side dishes
_____
_____
_____

Breads/Rolls
_____
_____
_____

Beverages
_____
_____
_____

Liquor
_____
_____
_____

Desserts
_____
_____
_____

Condiments
_____

Mints/Nuts
_____

Wedding cake
_____

Self-Catered Reception Shopping List

ITEM	QUANTITY	COST	STORE

Meats

_____ _____ _____ _____
_____ _____ _____ _____
_____ _____ _____ _____
_____ _____ _____ _____

Vegetables

_____ _____ _____ _____
_____ _____ _____ _____
_____ _____ _____ _____
_____ _____ _____ _____

Fruits

_____ _____ _____ _____
_____ _____ _____ _____
_____ _____ _____ _____
_____ _____ _____ _____

Bread, Rolls, Crackers

_____ _____ _____ _____
_____ _____ _____ _____
_____ _____ _____ _____
_____ _____ _____ _____

Cheese, Dips, Dairy

_____ _____ _____ _____
_____ _____ _____ _____
_____ _____ _____ _____
_____ _____ _____ _____

Self-Catered Reception Shopping List ──────

ITEM	QUANTITY	COST	STORE

Salads

_____	_____	_____	_____
_____	_____	_____	_____
_____	_____	_____	_____
_____	_____	_____	_____
_____	_____	_____	_____

Hors d'oeuvres

_____	_____	_____	_____
_____	_____	_____	_____
_____	_____	_____	_____
_____	_____	_____	_____
_____	_____	_____	_____

Beverages

_____	_____	_____	_____
_____	_____	_____	_____
_____	_____	_____	_____
_____	_____	_____	_____

Desserts, Pastries

_____	_____	_____	_____
_____	_____	_____	_____
_____	_____	_____	_____
_____	_____	_____	_____

Self-Catered Reception Shopping List

ITEM	QUANTITY	COST	STORE

Condiments

Serviceware (plates, napkins, silverware, cups, etc.)

Menu

The Wedding Cake

WEDDING CAKE TIPS

Select a bakery or caterer for your wedding cake at least four to five months before the wedding. Ask friends and family members for referrals. Also, ask wedding professionals for their recommendations. Use the *Wedding Vendors Referral Form* (pages 63–64) to keep track of and follow up with referrals. Bridal shows are a good place to meet with bakeries. They usually have photo albums showing wedding cakes they have created, along with cake samples for you to taste. Collect their brochures and business cards and keep them in the pockets provided in this wedding planner.

Start collecting pictures of wedding cakes from bridal magazines that appeal to you to show your baker.

As you are selecting a bakery, look over their photo album of cake designs and schedule a cake-tasting session to help ensure the best hiring decision.

Before ordering your cake, consider the following:

- What style of wedding are you having: casual, semi-formal, formal?
- Will your reception be indoors or outdoors?
- What colors are in your wedding?
- How many guests will be attending the reception?
- Do you want leftover cake for family and friends?
- Will you be saving the top tier for your first wedding anniversary?
- Do you want something traditional or something unique?
- Do you want simple or elaborate decorations?
- Do you want fresh flowers for decorations?
- Do you want a tiered cake or a sheet cake style?

Cakes are usually priced on a cost-per-serving basis. When deciding on the size of cake to order, consider if you will be saving the top tier for your first anniversary. Also consider the time of your reception, as it will affect how much cake your guests will eat. People usually eat more cake at afternoon receptions than they do at evening receptions. (Guests usually fill up with a full-course dinner at evening receptions.)

Once you have selected a bakery or caterer, place an order for your wedding cake. Get everything in writing and sign a contract! Pay the smallest deposit you can and pay with a credit card. Use the *Wedding Cake Worksheet* (page 166–68) as a letter of agreement. This worksheet describes the products and services your bakery or caterer provides.

The wedding cake should be delivered and set up at the reception site. Ask your baker about their delivery and setup fees. Also, find out about deposits on cake pillars and plates and if the deposit is refunded when you return the items.

Coordinate with the reception site director what time the cake can be delivered, where it will be displayed and who will cut and serve it. Your cake should be displayed on its own decorated table.

Delegate the following duties to responsible individuals, if your reception site or caterer does not provide these services (see: *List of Reception Helpers,* page 175):

- Decorating the cake table
- Cutting and serving the wedding cake
- Preserving the top layer of the wedding cake
- Returning the cake stands and pillars to the bakery

CAKE KNIFE AND SERVER

The cake knife and server are displayed on the cake table.

You can purchase beautifully decorated cake knife and server sets. Consider having them engraved with your names and wedding date.

Make sure someone is responsible for getting the cake knife and server set to the reception site, placing them on the cake table and picking them up after the reception is over.

CAKE TOP DECORATION

A miniature bride and groom is the traditional cake top. Other selections include: blown glass symbols such as rings, bells or doves, fresh or silk flowers, or check with a craft store about making your own.

If you decide to use fresh flowers as a cake top, have your florist coordinate the details with your baker.

Make sure someone is responsible for getting the cake top to the bakery or reception site. They also need to retrieve it at the end of the reception so you can keep it.

CAKE-CUTTING CEREMONY

Let the photographer, videographer and Master of Ceremonies know when the cake-cutting ceremony will take place.

At the cake-cutting ceremony, the groom puts his right hand over yours as you both cut the bottom layer of the cake. You then offer each other a bite. The helpers will cut and serve the rest of the cake to your guests.

AFTER THE WEDDING

It is customary to save the top layer of the wedding cake to share on your first wedding anniversary. The top layer should be removed after the bride and groom have cut the first slice, before the cake is served to the guests. To keep it fresh, place the cake in a box, wrap the box in aluminum foil, then enclose the whole thing in a layer of plastic. Two days before you plan to eat it, place it in the refrigerator to thaw.

THE GROOM'S CAKE

The groom's cake is usually a chocolate or spice cake served in a variety of shapes representing a groom's favorite sport or hobby. It can be served at the rehearsal dinner, at the wedding reception or placed in a box for the guests to take home.

It is perfectly acceptable to eliminate the groom's cake if you are on a tight budget.

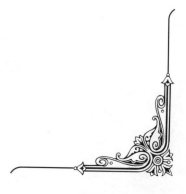

Wedding Cake Checklist

Due Date   **To Do**

❑ _____ Schedule consultations with bakeries 4-6 months before your wedding.

❑ _____ Select bakery, and order your cake 4-6 months before your wedding.

❑ _____ Order the groom's cake, if you decide to have one.

❑ _____ Make arrangements with the bakery for the delivery or pickup of the wedding cake.

❑ _____ Let the reception site know what time the cake will be delivered.

❑ _____ Make sure the reception site will have a decorated cake table, and decide where you want it located.

❑ _____ Purchase a decorated cake knife and server set.

❑ _____ Purchase a cake top decoration.

❑ _____ Decide when the cake cutting ceremony will take place.

❑ _____ Let your wedding professionals know when the cake cutting ceremony will take place:

❑ Master of Ceremonies ❑ Caterer
❑ Photographer ❑ Videographer
❑ Musicians ❑ Reception coordinator

❑ _____ If you are saving the top cake layer, make arrangements to have someone take it home and preserve it after the wedding.

❑ _____ Confirm who is responsible for cutting and serving the cake at the reception.

❑ _____ Make arrangements to have someone return the cake stands and pillars to the bakery after the wedding, if necessary.

❑ _____ Confirm major details of your cake order one month before your wedding.

❑ _____ Confirm all details of your cake order two weeks before your wedding.

Wedding Cake Worksheet

Bakery _____

Address_____

Phone_____ Contact _____ ☐ Confirmed

Date ordered _____

Delivery Person _____ Phone _____

Delivery date _____ Delivery time_____

Delivery location_____

Setup location_____

The Wedding Cake

Number of guests to be served _____

☐ Yes, we will be saving the top layer

Size _____ Shape _____ # of tiers _____

Decoration / Description _____

_____

_____

	Tier #1	Tier #2	Tier #3
Flavor	_____	_____	_____
Filling	_____	_____	_____
Icing	_____	_____	_____

Anniversary Tier

Flavor _____ Icing _____

Decoration / Description _____

_____

_____

_____

THE GROOM'S CAKE

Number of guests to be served _____ Pickup/delivery _____

Size _____ Shape _____

Flavor _____ Icing _____

Decoration / Description _____

_____

_____

Cake Accessories

Cake top decoration _____

Cake decorations _____

Cake flowers _____

Cake stands and pillars _____

Cake knife and server _____

Cake knife and server decorations _____

Cake boxes _____

Person Responsible for:

Provide cake knife and server _____

Decorate cake knife and server _____

Take cake knife and server to reception _____

Take cake top decoration to bakery or reception site _____

Delivery of cake to reception _____

Cake setup _____

Decorating cake table _____

Announce cake cutting ceremony _____

Provide cake cutting instructions _____

Cutting the cake _____

Cake servers _____

Saving/freezing top tier _____

Return cake stands and pillars to bakery _____

Planning the Reception

COST

Budget_____ Actual _____

Paid by: ❑ Credit Card ❑ Check ❑ Cash

Cost per serving _____ Flat fee _____

Delivery charge_____ Rental of cake stand/pillars _____

Groom's cake _____

Deposit _____ Date due _____ ❑ Deposit paid

Balance _____ Date due _____ ❑ Balance paid

Cancellation policy _____

_____   _____
Service Representative Signature   Date

_____   _____
Bridal Party Signature   Date

Use this worksheet as an agreement form and have the service representative sign and date it.

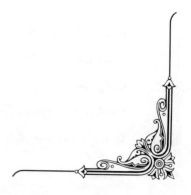

Reception Announcements ————————————

Have your Master of Ceremonies announce the following events:

Event	Time	Notes/Names
❑ Arrival of bride and groom	_____	_____
		_____
❑ Arrival of wedding party	_____	_____
		_____
		_____
		_____
		_____
		_____
		_____
		_____
❑ First dance	_____	_____
❑ Cake cutting ceremony	_____	_____
❑ Bouquet toss	_____	_____
❑ Garter removal and toss	_____	_____
❑ Bride and groom's exit	_____	_____
❑ Other:		
_____	_____	_____
_____	_____	_____
_____	_____	_____
_____	_____	_____
_____	_____	_____
_____	_____	_____
_____	_____	_____
_____	_____	_____
_____	_____	_____

Reception Floor Plan Layout ————————————————

SIZE AND NUMBER OF TABLES/CHAIRS NEEDED:

Head table _____ Guest tables _____

Cake table _____ Buffet tables _____

Guest book table _____ Gift table _____

Place card table _____ Guest tables _____

Prepare a diagram sketch showing the layout of the bride's table, parents' tables, buffet tables, cake table, gift table, guest register table, band location, dance floor, etc.:

Reception Seating Chart ————————————————

Table # _____

_____   _____
_____   _____
_____   _____
_____   _____
_____   _____

Table # _____

_____   _____
_____   _____
_____   _____
_____   _____
_____   _____

Table # _____

_____   _____
_____   _____
_____   _____
_____   _____
_____   _____

Table # _____

_____   _____
_____   _____
_____   _____
_____   _____
_____   _____

Table # _____

_____   _____
_____   _____
_____   _____
_____   _____
_____   _____

Table # _____

_____   _____
_____   _____
_____   _____
_____   _____

Table # _____

_____   _____
_____   _____
_____   _____
_____   _____
_____   _____

Table # _____

_____   _____
_____   _____
_____   _____
_____   _____
_____   _____

Table # _____

_____   _____
_____   _____
_____   _____
_____   _____
_____   _____

Table # _____

_____   _____
_____   _____
_____   _____
_____   _____
_____   _____

Table # _____

_____   _____
_____   _____
_____   _____
_____   _____

Table # _____

_____   _____
_____   _____
_____   _____
_____   _____

Reception Seating Chart ————————————

Table # _____

————————— —————————
————————— —————————
————————— —————————
————————— —————————

Table # _____

————————— —————————
————————— —————————
————————— —————————
————————— —————————

Table # _____

————————— —————————
————————— —————————
————————— —————————
————————— —————————

Table # _____

————————— —————————
————————— —————————
————————— —————————
————————— —————————

Table # _____

————————— —————————
————————— —————————
————————— —————————
————————— —————————

Table # _____

————————— —————————
————————— —————————
————————— —————————
————————— —————————

Table # _____

————————— —————————
————————— —————————
————————— —————————
————————— —————————

Table # _____

————————— —————————
————————— —————————
————————— —————————
————————— —————————

Table # _____

————————— —————————
————————— —————————
————————— —————————
————————— —————————

Table # _____

————————— —————————
————————— —————————
————————— —————————
————————— —————————

Table # _____

————————— —————————
————————— —————————
————————— —————————
————————— —————————

Table # _____

————————— —————————
————————— —————————
————————— —————————
————————— —————————

Please make duplicate copies if necessary

Reception Supply List

Item	Source/Description	Qty	Cost	Total
Guest register table				
Gift table				
Cake table				
Place card table				
Buffet tables				
Guest tables				
Chairs				
China dinnerware				
Plastic/paper dinnerware				
Silver flatware				
Plastic flatware				
China glassware				
Plastic glassware				
Cloth napkins				
Paper napkins				
Cloth tablecovers				
Plastic/paper tablecovers				
Serving bowls/dishes				
Utensils				
Trays				
Bubbles, rice, birdseed, flower petals to toss				
Audio equipment				
Microphone				
Lighting				
Mirror ball				
Dance floor				
Staging				
Portable bar				

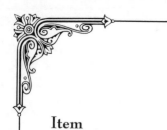

Planning the Reception

Item	Source/Description	Qty	Cost	Total
Coat/hat rack	_____	_____	_____	_____
Fans	_____	_____	_____	_____
Heaters	_____	_____	_____	_____
Tents	_____	_____	_____	_____
Umbrellas	_____	_____	_____	_____
Trash cans	_____	_____	_____	_____
Portable toilets	_____	_____	_____	_____
	_____	_____	_____	_____
	_____	_____	_____	_____
	_____	_____	_____	_____
	_____	_____	_____	_____
	_____	_____	_____	_____
	_____	_____	_____	_____

Total Supply Expenses $ _____

List of Reception Helpers ───────────────

Duties	Person Responsible
Reception coordinator	_____
Master of Ceremonies	_____
Setup and decoration helper(s)	_____
Photographer's assistant	_____
Videographer's assistant	_____
Take liquor to reception site	_____
Help set up the bar	_____
Bring and set up guest book, pen	_____
Guest register attendant	_____
Gift attendant	_____
Serve food and drinks	_____
Cut the wedding cake	_____
Serve wedding cake	_____
Give fee to musicians	_____
Take wedding gifts home	_____
Take bride's personal belongings home	_____
Take home flowers and decorations	_____
Pack-up guest book and take home	_____
Return unopened bottles of liquor	_____
Return cake stand and pillars to bakery	_____
Preserve top layer of wedding cake	_____
Cleanup	_____
Lockup reception site	_____
Return rental equipment	_____
Return groom's attire	_____
Take bride's gown to be cleaned	_____
Take bride's bouquet to be preserved	_____
_____	_____
_____	_____
_____	_____
_____	_____

Planning the Reception

Reception Timetable ——————————————————————

Time	Activity
_____	Reception coordinator arrives at reception site
_____	Florist arrives
_____	Helpers arrive
_____	Setup and decorating begins
_____	Caterer arrives
_____	Wedding cake table set up and decorated
_____	Wedding cake delivered and set up
_____	Musicians or DJ arrives and sets up
_____	Photographer arrives and sets up
_____	Videographer arrives and sets up
_____	Setup and decorating completed
_____	Parking attendants ready
_____	Music starts
_____	Guests arrive
_____	Wedding party arrives
_____	Announcement of the bride and groom
_____	Receiving line is formed
_____	Receiving line ends
_____	Guests are seated / have drinks for toasting
_____	Best man proposes first toast
_____	Food is served or buffet tables are set up and ready
_____	The first dance
_____	Dancing for guests begins
_____	Cake cutting ceremony
_____	Bride tosses the bouquet
_____	Groom removes and tosses the garter
_____	Bride changes into going-away outfit
_____	Transportation arrives for bride and groom
_____	Bride and groom's grand exit
_____	Last dance for guests
_____	Guests leave
_____	Tear-down and cleanup begins
_____	Rental company arrives to pick up rental items
_____	Reception over

Wedding Attire

Bride's Attire

Once you have decided on your wedding style and theme, start shopping for your wedding gown and accessories. Ask friends and family members for referrals to bridal salons. Also, ask wedding professionals for their recommendations. Use the *Wedding Vendors Referral Form* (pages 63-64) to keep track of and follow up with referrals. Bridal shows are a good place to view wedding dresses as they usually present a wedding fashion show. Collect brochures and business cards from the bridal salons represented in the fashion show and keep them in the pockets provided in this wedding planner.

Use the *Attire Shopping Worksheet* (page 181) to keep track of the stores you shopped at and the items they had that interested you. This will help to ensure the best buying decision.

Start collecting pictures of wedding dresses from bridal magazines that appeal to you.

Shop for your wedding gown six to twelve months before the wedding. Try to shop on a weekday when it is less crowded. Choose your gown before you select the bridesmaids' attire.

Once you have selected a wedding gown to order, get everything in writing and sign a contract! Pay the smallest you can and pay with a credit card. Use the *Bride's Wedding Attire Worksheet* (pages 182-183) as a letter of agreement. This worksheet describes the products and services your bridal salon provides.

Order your gown so it arrives at least six weeks before the wedding. When you pick up your gown, inspect it carefully before leaving the bridal salon.

Be sure to break in your new wedding shoes before the wedding.

Bridesmaids' Attire

Select the bridesmaids' dresses after the selection of your wedding gown. The style, color and material of your attendants' dresses should complement your wedding gown. Usually the bridesmaids are dressed alike, and the maid of honor is dressed differently. Try to select a dress that will look attractive on everyone and can be worn again for other occasions. Keep in mind the backs of the dresses, as that is what will be facing the guests throughout the ceremony.

Order your bridesmaids' dresses about six months ahead, especially if there are out-of-town bridesmaids and they will need their dresses sent to them for fittings. Dresses should be ordered at the same time to ensure dye lot match. If shoes need to be dyed, have them all dyed at the same shop.

Typically, attendants are responsible for purchasing their own dresses, accessories and shoes. You could consider paying a portion of the cost as a gift to the bridesmaids.

Alterations

Schedule alterations for you and your bridesmaids one month prior to the wedding. Take along the shoes and undergarments you will be wearing for the wedding. Ask the bridal salon if there is an extra charge for alterations.

Preserving Your Wedding Gown

To keep your wedding gown looking as beautiful as it did on your wedding day, have it professionally cleaned and preserved. Before taking it to a cleaner, carefully check the dress for stains from beverages, food and body oils, and point these out to your cleaner.

Bride's Mother

Traditionally, the bride's mother chooses her dress first, then calls the groom's mother to let her know what she will be wearing.

Men's Formal Wear

You and your fiancé select the style of formal wear the groom and his attendants

Wedding Attire

will wear. The attire is usually rented from a formal wear store. All groomsmen should be fitted at least six weeks prior to the wedding. Out-of-town groomsmen can go to a formal wear store in their area to be measured.

The father of the bride should dress similarly to the groomsmen. The father of the groom may dress in the same outfit as the others.

Typically, attendants are responsible for paying the rental fees for their attire.

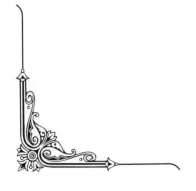

Wedding Attire Checklist ——————————————

Due Date   **To Do**

❑ _____ Order or purchase your attire:
    ❑ Wedding gown
    ❑ Veil/Headpiece

❑ _____ Purchase your attire accessories:
    ❑ Undergarments
    ❑ Hosiery
    ❑ Shoes
    ❑ Jewelry
    ❑ Something old, new, borrowed and blue

❑ _____ Select the attendants' attire and accessories:
    ❑ Dresses
    ❑ Headpiece
    ❑ Shoes
    ❑ Hosiery
    ❑ Jewelry
    ❑ Gloves

❑ _____ Record your fitting dates on the *Bride's Wedding Attire Worksheet.*

❑ _____ Schedule and record your attendants' fitting dates on the *Bridesmaids' Attire Worksheet.*

❑ _____ Make arrangements to have your gown picked up or delivered.

❑ _____ Make arrangements to have your gown pressed before the wedding.

❑ _____ Make arrangements to have your dress taken to be cleaned and preserved after the wedding.

❑ _____ Reserve the groom and his attendants' formal wear two to three months before the wedding.

❑ _____ Schedule and record the groom and his attendants' fitting dates on the *Men's Attire Information* page.

❑ _____ Make arrangements to have someone return the groom's formal wear after the wedding.

❑ _____ Pay any balance owing.

Attire Shopping Worksheet

Use this worksheet to record information about wedding gowns, bridesmaids' dresses, headpieces, shoes, accessories and lingerie.

Item	Description	Store	Cost

Bride's Wedding Attire Worksheet ———————————

Bridal salon _____

Address _____

Phone _____ Contact _____ ❏ Confirmed

Alterations person _____ Phone _____

Item	Description	Size	Cost
❏ Wedding gown	_____	_____	_____
❏ Veil/Headpiece	_____	_____	_____
❏ Shoes	_____	_____	_____
❏ Bra	_____	_____	_____
❏ Slip	_____	_____	_____
❏ Stockings	_____	_____	_____
❏ Garter	_____	_____	_____
❏ Gloves	_____	_____	_____
❏ Jewelry	_____	_____	_____
_____	_____	_____	_____
_____	_____	_____	_____
_____	_____	_____	_____

Date ordered _____ Date and time to pick up _____

Fitting dates _____

Alterations _____

Pressing the Gown

Who will be pressing the gown _____ Cost _____

Date _____ Time _____ Location _____

Instructions_____

Wedding Attire

Preserving the Gown

Who will be cleaning/preserving the gown _____ Cost _____

Date _____ Time _____ Location _____

Instructions_____

Cost

Budget_____ Actual_____

Paid by: ❑ Credit Card ❑ Check ❑ Cash

Tax_____ Gratuity _____

Deposit _____ Date due _____ ❑ Deposit paid

Balance _____ Date due _____ ❑ Balance paid

Cancellation policy _____

_____   _____

Service Representative Signature   Date

_____   _____

Bridal Party Signature   Date

Use this worksheet as an agreement form and have the service representative sign and date it.

Bridesmaids' Attire Worksheet ————————————————

Item	Description	Quantity/ Sizes to Order	Costs
Maid of honor			
Dress			
Headpiece			
Shoes			
Stockings			
Gloves			
Accessories			
Bridesmaids			
Dress			
Headpiece			
Shoes			
Stockings			
Gloves			
Accessories			
Flower girl			
Dress			
Headpiece			
Shoes			
Stockings			
Gloves			
Accessories			

Bride's Mother

Dress and shoes description _____

_____

Groom's Mother

Dress and shoes description _____

_____

Wedding Attire

Bridesmaids' Attire Information ———————————

Name _____

Measurements: bust _____ waist _____ hips _____ height _____

Sizes: dress _____ shoe _____ hat _____ glove _____

Date dress ordered _____ Date/time to pick up _____ Picked up _____

Fitting dates _____

Dress deposit paid _____ Balance due _____ Paid _____

Name _____

Measurements: bust _____ waist _____ hips _____ height _____

Sizes: dress _____ shoe _____ hat _____ glove _____

Date dress ordered _____ Date/time to pick up _____ Picked up _____

Fitting dates _____

Dress deposit paid _____ Balance due _____ Paid _____

Name _____

Measurements: bust _____ waist _____ hips _____ height _____

Sizes: dress _____ shoe _____ hat _____ glove _____

Date dress ordered _____ Date/time to pick up _____ Picked up _____

Fitting dates _____

Dress deposit paid _____ Balance due _____ Paid _____

Name _____

Measurements: bust _____ waist _____ hips _____ height _____

Sizes: dress _____ shoe _____ hat _____ glove _____

Date dress ordered _____ Date/time to pick up _____ Picked up _____

Fitting dates _____

Dress deposit paid _____ Balance due _____ Paid _____

Wedding Attire

Bridesmaids' Attire Information ———————————

Name _____

Measurements: bust _____ waist _____ hips _____ height _____

Sizes: dress _____ shoe _____ hat _____ glove _____

Date dress ordered _____ Date/time to pick up _____ Picked up _____

Fitting dates _____

Dress deposit paid_____ Balance due _____ Paid_____

Name _____

Measurements: bust _____ waist _____ hips _____ height _____

Sizes: dress _____ shoe _____ hat _____ glove _____

Date dress ordered _____ Date/time to pick up _____ Picked up _____

Fitting dates _____

Dress deposit paid_____ Balance due _____ Paid_____

Name _____

Measurements: bust _____ waist _____ hips _____ height _____

Sizes: dress _____ shoe _____ hat _____ glove _____

Date dress ordered _____ Date/time to pick up _____ Picked up _____

Fitting dates _____

Dress deposit paid_____ Balance due _____ Paid_____

Name _____

Measurements: bust _____ waist _____ hips _____ height _____

Sizes: dress _____ shoe _____ hat _____ glove _____

Date dress ordered _____ Date/time to pick up _____ Picked up _____

Fitting dates _____

Dress deposit paid_____ Balance due _____ Paid_____

Please make duplicate copies if necessary

Groom's Formal Wear Worksheet ——————————

Formal Wear Store _____

Address _____

Phone_____ Contact _____ ❑ Confirmed

Alterations person _____ Phone _____

Item	Description, Style #	Size	Cost
❑ Tuxedo	_____	_____	_____
❑ Shirt	_____	_____	_____
❑ Vest	_____	_____	_____
❑ Cummerbund	_____	_____	_____
❑ Tie	_____	_____	_____
❑ Ascot	_____	_____	_____
❑ Shoes	_____	_____	_____
❑ Socks	_____	_____	_____
❑ Suspenders	_____	_____	_____
❑ Cufflinks	_____	_____	_____
❑ Button studs	_____	_____	_____

Fitting dates _____

Date and time to pick up _____

Person responsible for picking up groom's formal wear _____

Date and time formal wear is to be returned _____

Person responsible for returning groom's formal wear _____

Cost

Budget _____ Actual _____ Paid by: ❑ Credit Card ❑ Check ❑ Cash

Alterations _____ Total formal wear expenses _____

Deposit _____ Date due _____ ❑ Deposit paid

Balance _____ Date due _____ ❑ Balance paid

Damage/stain policy _____

Cancellation policy _____

_____   _____

Service Representative Signature   Date

_____   _____

Bridal Party Signature   Date

Use this worksheet as an agreement form and have the service representative sign and date it.

Men's Attire Worksheet ————————————————

Store _____

Address_____

Phone _____ Contact _____ ❏ Confirmed

Alterations person _____ Phone _____

Item	Description	Quantity/ Sizes to Order	Costs
Best man			
Tuxedo	_____	_____	_____
Shirt	_____	_____	_____
Tie	_____	_____	_____
Shoes	_____	_____	_____
Socks	_____	_____	_____
Accessories	_____	_____	_____
Groomsmen			
Tuxedo	_____	_____	_____
Shirt	_____	_____	_____
Tie	_____	_____	_____
Shoes	_____	_____	_____
Socks	_____	_____	_____
Accessories	_____	_____	_____
Ring bearer			
Tuxedo	_____	_____	_____
Shirt	_____	_____	_____
Tie	_____	_____	_____
Shoes	_____	_____	_____
Socks	_____	_____	_____
Accessories	_____	_____	_____

Bride's Father

Formal wear description _____

_____

Groom's Father

Formal wear description _____

_____

Wedding Attire

Men's Attire Information ———————————————

Name _____

Measurements: neck _____ sleeve _____ waist _____ inseam_____

Sizes: coat _____ shirt _____ trousers _____ shoe _____

Date attire ordered_____ Date/time to pick up _____ Picked up _____

Fitting dates _____

Attire deposit paid_____ Balance due _____ Paid _____

Name _____

Measurements: neck _____ sleeve _____ waist _____ inseam_____

Sizes: coat _____ shirt _____ trousers _____ shoe _____

Date attire ordered_____ Date/time to pick up _____ Picked up _____

Fitting dates _____

Attire deposit paid_____ Balance due _____ Paid _____

Name _____

Measurements: neck _____ sleeve _____ waist _____ inseam_____

Sizes: coat _____ shirt _____ trousers _____ shoe _____

Date attire ordered_____ Date/time to pick up _____ Picked up _____

Fitting dates _____

Attire deposit paid_____ Balance due _____ Paid _____

Name _____

Measurements: neck _____ sleeve _____ waist _____ inseam_____

Sizes: coat _____ shirt _____ trousers _____ shoe _____

Date attire ordered_____ Date/time to pick up _____ Picked up _____

Fitting dates _____

Attire deposit paid_____ Balance due _____ Paid _____

Men's Attire Information

Name _____

Measurements: neck _____ sleeve _____ waist _____ inseam_____

Sizes: coat _____ shirt _____ trousers _____ shoe _____

Date attire ordered_____ Date/time to pick up _____ Picked up _____

Fitting dates _____

Attire deposit paid _____ Balance due _____ Paid _____

Name _____

Measurements: neck _____ sleeve _____ waist _____ inseam_____

Sizes: coat _____ shirt _____ trousers _____ shoe _____

Date attire ordered_____ Date/time to pick up _____ Picked up _____

Fitting dates _____

Attire deposit paid _____ Balance due _____ Paid _____

Name _____

Measurements: neck _____ sleeve _____ waist _____ inseam_____

Sizes: coat _____ shirt _____ trousers _____ shoe _____

Date attire ordered_____ Date/time to pick up _____ Picked up _____

Fitting dates _____

Attire deposit paid _____ Balance due _____ Paid _____

Name _____

Measurements: neck _____ sleeve _____ waist _____ inseam_____

Sizes: coat _____ shirt _____ trousers _____ shoe _____

Date attire ordered_____ Date/time to pick up _____ Picked up _____

Fitting dates _____

Attire deposit paid _____ Balance due _____ Paid _____

Please make duplicate copies if necessary

Flowers and Decorations

Wedding Flower Tips

As soon as the wedding date is set, and the ceremony and reception sites are reserved, start interviewing florists. Ask friends and family members for referrals. Also, ask wedding professionals for their recommendations. Use the *Wedding Vendors Referral Form* (pages 63-64) to keep track of and follow up with referrals. Collect their brochures and business cards and keep them in the envelopes provided in this wedding planner.

Select and reserve your florist six to twelve months before the wedding. Use the *Selecting a Florist* (pages 194-95) form to help ensure the best hiring decision.

Ask for at least three references from potential florists and follow up with each one.

Ask potential florists if you can view pictures of other weddings they have done.

Hire someone who specializes in weddings, preferably someone who is familiar with your ceremony and reception sites. Some florists can also provide decorating services. The florist you select should be happy to visit your ceremony and reception sites and make recommendations, if necessary.

Once you have selected a florist for your wedding, get everything in writing and sign a contract! Pay the smallest deposit you can and pay with a credit card. Use the *Floral Worksheet* (pages 197-98) as a letter of agreement. This worksheet describes the products and services your florist provides.

Flowers and Decorations

Set an appointment to meet with your florist and go over the details. Provide your florist with information about your wedding: your budget for flowers and decorations, the ceremony and reception sites, time of day, style of your gown and the color of your bridesmaids' dresses. Take along fabric swatches and photos of flowers you have in mind.

Ask the ceremony and reception sites about restrictions regarding flowers and decorations before making any final decorating decisions.

Delegate someone to be responsible for distributing flowers to the bridal party, taking ceremony flowers to the reception and taking the flowers after the reception. They will also need to return any rental equipment to the florist.

If you're having photos taken before the ceremony, coordinate this with your florist so the flowers arrive in time.

Purchase a silk floral toss bouquet so your wedding bouquet can be preserved. Consider presenting the bridesmaids with silk bouquets as a keepsake of your wedding.

Flower Selections

Determine the style and color scheme of your wedding before selecting your flowers. Keep in mind the time of year and what flowers are available.

The bridesmaids' bouquets should coordinate with your bouquet, the theme of the wedding and their dresses. The maid or matron of honor's bouquet is usually a little larger than the bridesmaids', and may be of a different color.

Traditionally the flower girl carries a basket filled with flower petals and scatters them in the bride's path. Check with your ceremony site about any restrictions.

The mothers and grandmothers traditionally wear a corsage. Consider their dress colors and style when selecting each corsage.

The groom and ushers each wear a boutonniere on the left lapel. The groom's boutonniere should look a little different.

Year-Round Flowers—Baby's Breath, Carnations, Orchids, Roses.

Winter Flowers—Amaryllis, Chrysanthemums, Poinsettias.

Spring Flowers—Amaryllis, Anemones, Calla Lilies, Daffodils, Day Lilies, Delphiniums, Forget-me-nots, Gardenias, Lilacs, Lilies of the Valley, Violets, Tulips.

Summer Flowers—Anemones, Asters, Bachelor Buttons, Calla Lilies, Daisies, Delphiniums, Irises, Lilies, Stephanotis, Strawflowers.

Fall Flowers—Anemones, Calla Lilies, Chrysanthemums, Daisies, Day Lilies, Delphiniums.

Flower Preservation

It is important to consider floral preservation when you begin planning your wedding flowers. You will want to select flowers for your bouquet that preserve well. Make arrangements for having your bouquet preserved well in advance, since your floral preservationist will want to begin processing your flowers as soon as possible after the wedding.

Flowers recommended for preservation include: Alstromeria, Baby's Breath, Casablanca Lilies, Delphiniums, Dendrobium Orchids, Freesias, Queen Anne's Lace, Roses, Stargazer Liliies, Stock, Gerbera Daisies, Heather, Irises, Monte Casino, Snapdragons.

Flowers that do not traditionally preserve well include Chrysanthemums, some daisies, Anthuriums, and some tropical flowers. Red roses and other red flowers tend to preserve a very dark red.

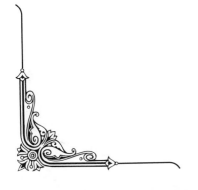

Flowers and Decorations

Selecting a Florist ————————————————————

Estimate #1

Appointment date _____ Time _____

Business _____

Address _____

_____

Contact _____ Phone _____

My budget for flowers $ _____

Estimated total cost $ _____

Delivery and setup charges $ _____

Deposit required $ _____

Cancellation policy _____

References _____

Questions to Ask

What products and services can you provide:

❑ Fresh flowers   ❑ Silk flowers
❑ Dried flowers   ❑ Rented plants

Are you willing to visit my ceremony and reception
sites and make recommendations? _____

Have you done a wedding at my ceremony site?
reception site?_____

Will you deliver and set the flowers up at the
sites? _____

Will you work with my caterer and bakery on
floral decorations? _____

Can you preserve my bridal bouquet? _____

Other services they can provide _____

_____

_____

Comments _____

_____

_____

_____

_____

Please make duplicate copies if necessary

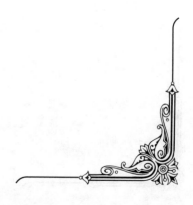

194

Selecting a Florist

Estimate #2

Appointment date _____ Time _____

Business _____

Address _____

_____

Contact _____ Phone _____

My budget for flowers $ _____

Estimated total cost $ _____

Delivery and setup charges $ _____

Deposit required $ _____

Cancellation policy _____

References _____

Questions to Ask

What products and services can you provide:

❑ Fresh flowers ❑ Silk flowers
❑ Dried flowers ❑ Rented plants

Are you willing to visit my ceremony and reception sites and make recommendations? _____

Have you done a wedding at my ceremony site? reception site?_____

Will you deliver and set the flowers up at the sites? _____

Will you work with my caterer and bakery on floral decorations? _____

Can you preserve my bridal bouquet? _____

Other services they can provide _____

_____

_____

Comments _____

_____

_____

_____

_____

Please make duplicate copies if necessary

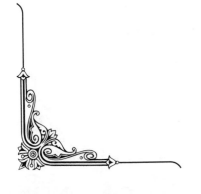

Wedding Flowers Checklist ——————————

Due Date   **To Do**

❑ _____ Check with your ceremony and reception sites about any floral/decorating restrictions they have.

❑ _____ Hire a professional florist six to twelve months before the wedding.

❑ _____ Sign agreements and pay deposits.

❑ _____ Decide on the type of flowers you want:
    ❑ Fresh flowers
    ❑ Dried flowers
    ❑ Silk flowers

❑ _____ Select flowers for the following:
    ❑ Bride's bouquet
    ❑ Attendants' flowers
    ❑ Groom's boutonniere
    ❑ Ushers' and groomsmen's boutonnieres
    ❑ Flowers for family members
    ❑ Flowers for helpers
    ❑ Floral decorations for the ceremony site
    ❑ Floral decorations for the reception site

❑ _____ Make arrangements to have your bouquet preserved.

❑ _____ Recruit someone to be responsible for taking the delivered flowers to the appropriate people: bride, bridesmaids, groom, groomsmen, etc.

❑ _____ Confirm major details of your floral order the month before your wedding.

❑ _____ Confirm all details of your floral order two weeks before your wedding.

Floral Worksheet ——————————————————

Florist _____

Address _____

Phone _____ Contact _____ ❑ Confirmed

Alterations person _____ Phone _____

Flower Selection
❑ Fresh flowers   ❑ Dried flowers   ❑ Silk flowers

Ceremony Flowers: Delivery Information
❑ Flowers will be delivered

Delivery date _____ Time _____ Person responsible_____

Delivery location_____

Reception Flowers: Delivery Information
❑ Flowers will be delivered

Delivery date _____ Time _____ Person responsible _____

Delivery location_____

Pickup Information
❑ Flowers need to be picked up

Pickup date _____ Time _____ Person responsible _____

Delivery location_____

Ask about:

Rental services/equipment _____

Decorating services _____

Familiar with your wedding and reception sites _____

Able to preserve your bridal bouquet _____

Able to work with caterer and bakery on floral decorations _____

Flowers and Decorations

Cost

Budget _____ Actual _____

Paid by: ❑ Credit Card ❑ Check ❑ Cash

Bride's bouquet_____ Attendants' flowers _____

Corsages _____ Boutonnieres _____

Ceremony flowers_____ Reception flowers _____

Floral preservation _____

Other charges _____

Deposit _____ Date due _____ ❑ Deposit paid

Balance _____ Date due _____ ❑ Balance paid

Cancellation policy _____

_____ _____

Service Representative Signature   Date

_____ _____

Bridal Party Signature   Date

Use this worksheet as an agreement form and have the service representative sign and date it.

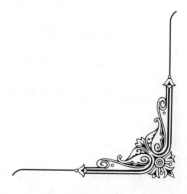

Floral Checklist

Item	Description	Quantity	Cost	Total
Bride's flowers	_____	_____	_____	_____
Bouquet	_____	_____	_____	_____
Bouquet for tossing	_____	_____	_____	_____
Floral headpiece	_____	_____	_____	_____
Going-away corsage	_____	_____	_____	_____

Attendants' Bouquets

Maid of honor's bouquet	_____	_____	_____	_____
Maid of honor's headpiece	_____	_____	_____	_____
Bridesmaids' bouquets	_____	_____	_____	_____
Bridesmaids' headpieces	_____	_____	_____	_____
Jr. bridesmaid's bouquet	_____	_____	_____	_____
Jr. bridesmaid's headpiece	_____	_____	_____	_____
Flower girl's basket	_____	_____	_____	_____
Flower girl's headpiece	_____	_____	_____	_____

Boutonnieres

Groom's boutonniere	_____	_____	_____	_____
Best man's boutonniere	_____	_____	_____	_____
Groomsmen's boutonnieres	_____	_____	_____	_____
Ushers' boutonnieres	_____	_____	_____	_____
Ring bearer's boutonniere	_____	_____	_____	_____
Train bearer's boutonniere	_____	_____	_____	_____

Family Flowers

Mothers' corsages	_____	_____	_____	_____
Fathers' boutonnieres	_____	_____	_____	_____

Helpers' Flowers

Bridal consultant	_____	_____	_____	_____
Hostess	_____	_____	_____	_____

Flowers and Decorations

Floral Checklist

Item	Description	Quantity	Cost	Total
Guest register attendant				
Gift attendant				
Cake cutter and servers				

Ceremony Flowers

Item	Description	Quantity	Cost	Total
Arch / Canopy				
Altar				
Candelabras				
Pews				
Aisles				
Windows				

Reception Flowers

Item	Description	Quantity	Cost	Total
Bride's table				
Attendants' tables				
Parents' tables				
Guests' tables				
Buffet table				
Cake table				
Guest register table				
Gift table				
Champagne/punch table				
Wedding cake				
Top of wedding cake				

Decorations Worksheet ⸺

Party Store_____

Address_____

Phone _____ Contact _____ ❏ Confirmed

Alterations person _____Phone _____

Wedding Colors _____

Wedding Theme/Style _____

Ceremony Decorating Ideas

_____

_____

_____

_____

_____

Reception Table Centerpieces

_____

_____

_____

_____

Reception Decorating Ideas

_____

_____

_____

_____

_____

_____

Decorations Checklist

Item	Description	Quantity	Cost	Total
Balloons				
Helium tank				
Bells				
Baskets				
Bows				
Hearts				
Doves				
Umbrella				
Ribbon				
Streamers				
Banners				
Confetti				
Garland				
"Just Married" sign				
Champagne fountain				
Ice sculpture				
Candles				
Mirror ball				

Decorative Rentals

Table centerpieces				
Mail card box				
Decorative pillars				
Decorative columns				
Statuaries				
Trellises				
Latticework				
Potted plants				
Potted flowers				

Wedding Music

Through the selection of music for the ceremony, you set the mood for your wedding and express your feelings about marriage.

Ceremony Music Tips

As soon as the wedding date is set, and the ceremony site is reserved, begin auditioning musicians. Ask friends and family members for referrals. Also, ask wedding professionals for their recommendations. Use the *Wedding Vendors Referral Form* (pages 63-64) to keep track of and follow up with referrals. Bridal shows are a good place to meet professional musicians and vocalists and hear them perform or view a videotape of a recent wedding they performed at. Collect their brochures and business cards and keep them in the pockets provided in this wedding planner.

Ask the ceremony site director about restrictions regarding music before you hire musicians or vocalists. Go over your musical selections with your officiant as they will have their own rules about ceremony music.

Select and reserve musicians and vocalists six to twelve months before the wedding. Use the *Selecting Ceremony Musicians* (pages 206-7) form to ensure the best hiring decision.

Your church may have a resident organist, or you may want to hire outside musicians.

Ask for at least three references from potential musicians and vocalists and follow up with each one.

Wedding Music

Ask potential musicians and vocalists to view a videotape of a recent wedding they performed at, or hear an audio tape before booking them.

Once you have selected musicians for the ceremony, get everything in writing and sign a contract! Pay the smallest deposit you can and pay with a credit card. Use the *Ceremony Music Worksheet* (pages 208-9) as a letter of agreement. This worksheet describes the services your musicians and vocalists provide.

Ask your musicians what they require in terms of space, rehearsal time, setup time, electrical outlets and amplification equipment.

Select the ceremony music at least two months before your wedding. Go over the *Ceremony Music Selections* (page 210) with your musicians, vocalists and officiant and give each of them a copy. This page shows which music you have selected for each section of your ceremony and what time it is to be played.

Wedding music is divided into four main sections:

THE PRELUDE
The prelude sets the mood of your wedding and usually begins thirty minutes before the ceremony starts, as the guests are being seated.

THE PROCESSIONAL
The processional is played as the mothers of the bride and groom and the wedding party come down the aisle.

DURING THE CEREMONY
During the ceremony, consider playing special songs during the lighting of the altar candles, lighting of the unity candle, when you leave your father and go to the groom, after scripture readings or prayers, during communion and after the kiss.

THE RECESSIONAL
The recessional is played as you walk down the aisle as husband and wife. It should be joyous and exciting.

Plan how you will start the processional music. The time you have planned on the *Ceremony Music Selections* page may change due to late arriving guests or other delays. The ceremony coordinator should be aware of any delays and keep you informed. When everyone is ready to go, the ceremony coordinator informs the father of the bride or the officiant, who in turn signals the musicians to start the processional music.

Wedding Music

Ceremony Music Checklist

Due Date	To Do

❑ _____ Check with the ceremony site for any music restrictions it may have.

❑ _____ Check with officiant for any music restrictions he/she may have.

❑ _____ Interview and audition a variety of musicians. (See: *Selecting Ceremony Musicians*)

❑ _____ Interview and audition soloists. (See: *Selecting Ceremony Musicians*)

❑ _____ Book musicians. (See: *Ceremony Music Worksheet*)

❑ _____ Book soloist. (See: *Ceremony Music Worksheet*)

❑ _____ Sign agreements and pay deposits.

❑ _____ Make music selections. (See: *Ceremony Music Selections*)

❑ _____ Give a copy of the *Ceremony Music Selections* page to:
- ❑ Officiant
- ❑ Musicians
- ❑ Vocalist
- ❑ Ceremony coordinator

❑ _____ Invite musicians to the ceremony rehearsal.

❑ _____ Confirm major ceremony music details one month before your wedding.

❑ _____ Confirm all ceremony music details two weeks before your wedding.

❑ _____ Pay any balance owing on contracts.

Ceremony Instrumentation Examples:

- Organist
- Vocalist
- Harpist
- Pianist
- Guitarist

- Harp/Flute
- Harp/Violin
- Harp/Piano
- Guitar/Flute
- Pianist/Guitarist

- String quartet
- String trio
- Flute trio
- Brass ensembles
- Harpsichord

- Woodwind
- Dulcimer
- Trumpeters

Wedding Music

Selecting Ceremony Musicians

Estimate #1

Appointment date _____ Time _____

Business _____

Address _____

_____

Contact _____ Phone _____

My budget for ceremony music $ _____

Estimated total cost $ _____

Deposit required $ _____

Cancellation policy _____

References _____

_____

❑ Auditioned person(s) who would playing at my ceremony.

❑ Picked up price list and brochure.

Questions to Ask

Are you available at the date and time of my wedding? _____

Are you familiar with my ceremony site? _____

How many years have you been playing for weddings? _____

What style of music do you play? _____

_____

Will you take special requests? _____

What instruments would you be playing? _____

_____

_____

How many musicians would be there? _____

What type of equipment do you provide? _____

_____

What equipment would you need? _____

_____

Do you need any electrical outlets? _____

What are your space requirements? _____

_____

What do you normally wear at weddings? _____

_____

Would you be willing to wear specified attire? _____

Prices

Hourly rate _____

Flat fee _____

Gratuity and taxes _____

Overtime rate _____

Flat fee _____

Gratuity and taxes _____

Overtime rate _____

Please make duplicate copies if necessary

Selecting Ceremony Musicians ————————

Estimate #2

Appointment date _____ Time _____

Business _____

Address _____

_____

Contact _____ Phone _____

My budget for ceremony music $ _____

Estimated total cost $ _____

Deposit required $ _____

Cancellation policy _____

References _____

_____

❏ Auditioned person(s) who would playing at my ceremony.

❏ Picked up price list and brochure.

Questions to Ask

Are you available at the date and time of my wedding? _____

Are you familiar with my ceremony site? _____

How many years have you been playing for weddings? _____

What style of music do you play? _____

_____

Will you take special requests? _____

What instruments would you be playing? _____

_____

_____

How many musicians would be there? _____

What type of equipment do you provide? _____

_____

What equipment would you need? _____

_____

Do you need any electrical outlets? _____

What are your space requirements? _____

_____

What do you normally wear at weddings? _____

_____

Would you be willing to wear specified attire? ____

Prices

Hourly rate _____

Flat fee _____

Gratuity and taxes _____

Overtime rate _____

Flat fee _____

Gratuity and taxes _____

Overtime rate _____

Please make duplicate copies if necessary

Ceremony Music Worksheet ————————————————

Musicians

Group_____

Address_____

Phone_____ Contact _____ ❑ Confirmed

Vocalist

Group_____

Address _____

Phone_____ Contact _____ ❑ Confirmed

Ceremony Music Information

Rehearsal date_____ Time _____ Location _____

Wedding date _____ Time _____ Location _____

Ceremony music restrictions _____

Instruments provided/needed _____

Musician's arrival time _____ Vocalist's arrival time_____

Setup time/location _____ Music start time _____

Musician's/Vocalist's attire _____

Wedding Music

COST – MUSICIANS

Budget _____ Actual _____

Paid by: ❏ Credit Card   ❏ Check   ❏ Cash

Musician's fee _____ Overtime rate _____ Gratuity _____

Deposit _____ Date due _____ ❏ Deposit paid

Balance _____ Date due _____ ❏ Balance paid

Cancellation policy _____

_____

_____   _____
Musician's Signature   Date

_____   _____
Bridal Party Signature   Date

Use this worksheet as an agreement form and have the service representative sign and date it.

COST – VOCALIST

Budget _____ Actual _____

Paid by: ❏ Credit Card   ❏ Check   ❏ Cash

Musician's fee _____ Overtime rate _____ Gratuity _____

Deposit _____ Date due _____ ❏ Deposit paid

Balance _____ Date due _____ ❏ Balance paid

Cancellation policy _____

_____   _____
Vocalist's Signature   Date

_____   _____
Bridal Party Signature   Date

Use this worksheet as an agreement form and have the service representative sign and date it.

Wedding Music

Ceremony Music Selections

Activity	Time / Cue	Selection
Prelude	_____	_____
	_____	_____
	_____	_____
First solo	_____	_____
Second solo	_____	_____
Processional	_____	_____
	_____	_____
Bride's entrance	_____	_____
During ceremony	_____	_____
	_____	_____
	_____	_____
	_____	_____
	_____	_____
	_____	_____
Recessional	_____	_____
	_____	_____
	_____	_____
Postlude	_____	_____
	_____	_____
	_____	_____

Reception Music

RECEPTION MUSIC TIPS

As soon as the wedding date is set, and the reception site is reserved, begin auditioning musicians. Ask friends and family members for referrals. Also, ask wedding professionals for their recommendations. Use the *Wedding Vendors Referral Form* (pages 63-64) to keep track of and follow up with referrals. Bridal shows are a good place to meet professional musicians and disc jockeys and hear them perform or view a videotape of a recent wedding they performed did. Collect their brochures and business cards and keep them in the envelopes provided in this wedding planner.

Ask the reception site director about restrictions regarding music and dancing before hiring musicians, a band or a DJ.

Select and reserve reception musicians six to twelve months before the wedding. Use the *Selecting Reception Musicians* (pages 213-14) form to ensure the best hiring decision.

Ask for at least three references from potential musicians, bands and disc jockeys and follow up with each one.

Ask potential musicians to view a videotape of a recent wedding they performed at, or ask if you can attend an upcoming performance.

Once you have selected musicians for the reception, get everything in writing and sign a contract! Pay the smallest deposit you can and pay with a credit card. Use the *Reception Music Worksheet* (page 215) as a letter of agreement. This worksheet describes the services your musicians provide.

Find out if the band leader will act as Master of Ceremonies. Complete the *Reception Announcements* sheet (page 169). Go over the events you want announced with the Master of Ceremonies one month before the wedding.

Ask your musicians what they require in terms of space, rehearsal time, setup time, electrical outlets and amplification equipment.

Ask your musicians if your guests will be able to make special song requests, or if their routine is preset.

Find out how many breaks the musicians will be taking and how long each break is. Make arrangements to have background music playing during their breaks.

Wedding Music

Let your caterer know if you will be providing refreshments to the musicians.

Make your selection of music that will be played during key moments of your reception at least two months before your wedding. Go over the *Reception Music Selections* (page 216) with your musicians and give each of them a copy. This page shows which music you have selected for different activities that happen during your reception and what time it is to be played.

The musicians need to arrive and be ready to play before your guests start arriving at the reception. The music should be playing as the guests are entering the reception site.

Reception Music Examples:

- Country-western
- '50s
- Bluegrass
- Cajun
- Reggae

- Top 40
- Swing
- Blues
- Motown
- Classical

- Big band
- Rock 'n' roll
- Jazz
- Disc jockey
- Karaoke

Reception Music Checklist

Due Date	To Do
❏ _____	Check with the reception site for any music restrictions it may have.
❏ _____	Interview and audition a variety of bands/musicians. (See: *Selecting Reception Musicians*)
❏ _____	Book musicians. (See: *Reception Music Worksheet)*
❏ _____	Sign agreements and pay deposits.
❏ _____	Make music selections. (See: *Reception Music Selections*)
❏ _____	Go over timing of announcements with the band leader or your Master of Ceremonies. (See: *Reception Announcements,* page 169)
❏ _____	Give a copy of the *Reception Music Selections* page to: ❏ Musicians ❏ Reception coordinator
❏ _____	Confirm major reception music details one month before your wedding.
❏ _____	Confirm all reception music details two weeks before your wedding.
❏ _____	Pay any balance owing on contracts.

Wedding Music

Reception Music Worksheet ————————————————

RECEPTION MUSIC

❏ Instrumentalist ❏ Band ❏ Disc jockey ❏ _____

Name _____

Address_____

Phone _____ Contact _____ ❏ Confirmed

Reception Music Information

Reception date_____ Time_____ Location_____

Type/style of music you will play _____

Will you take special requests? _____

Reception site music restrictions _____

Musician's arrival/setup time _____

Setup location _____

Music to begin at: start time _____ end time _____

Available to play longer if needed? _____

Number and length of breaks _____

Do you provide recorded music during breaks? _____

Do we provide refreshments to you during breaks? _____

Will you act as Master of Ceremonies? _____

Number of musicians _____

Musician's wedding day attire _____

Instruments provided/needed _____

Electrical outlet needs _____

Special effects you provide _____

Cost

Budget _____ Actual _____

Paid by: ❏ Credit Card ❏ Check ❏ Cash

Musician's fee _____ Overtime rate_____ Gratuity _____

Deposit _____ Date due _____ ❏ Deposit paid

Balance _____ Date due _____ ❏ Balance paid

Cancellation policy _____

_____   _____
Service Representative Signature   Date

_____   _____
Bridal Party Signature   Date

Use this worksheet as an agreement form and have the service representatives sign and date it.

Selecting Reception Musicians

Estimate #1

Appointment date_____ Time_____

Business _____

Address _____

Contact_____ Phone_____

My budget for reception music $_____

Estimated total cost $ _____

Deposit required $ _____

Cancellation policy _____

References _____

_____

❑ Auditioned person(s) who would playing at my ceremony.

❑ Picked up price list and brochure.

Type of Entertainment

❑ Instrumentalist   ❑ Band

❑ Disc jockey   ❑ _____

Questions to Ask

Are you available at the date and time of my wedding?

_____

Are you familiar with my reception site? _____

How many years have you been playing for weddings?__

What style of music do you play? _____

Will you take special requests? _____

What instruments would you be playing? _____

_____

_____

How many musicians would be there? _____

What type of equipment do you provide? _____

_____

_____

What equipment would you need? _____

_____

_____

Do you need any electrical outlets? _____

What are your space requirements? _____

_____

How much time do you need to set up? _____

Do you provide any special effects, lighting? _____

What do you normally wear at weddings? _____

Would you be willing to wear specified attire? _____

Can you act as Master of Ceremonies? _____

How many breaks do you take? _____

How long are the breaks? _____

Do you provide background music during your breaks? _____

Prices

Hourly rate _____

Flat fee _____

Gratuity and taxes _____

Overtime rate _____

Comments_____

_____

Please make duplicate copies if necessary

Selecting Reception Musicians
Estimate #2

Appointment date_____ Time_____

Business _____

Address _____

Contact_____ Phone_____

My budget for reception music $_____

Estimated total cost $ _____

Deposit required $ _____

Cancellation policy _____

References _____

_____

❑ Auditioned person(s) who would playing at my ceremony.

❑ Picked up price list and brochure.

Type of Entertainment

❑ Instrumentalist ❑ Band

❑ Disc jockey ❑ _____

Questions to Ask

Are you available at the date and time of my wedding?

_____

Are you familiar with my reception site? _____

How many years have you been playing for weddings?__

What style of music do you play? _____

Will you take special requests? _____

What instruments would you be playing?_____

_____

_____

How many musicians would be there? _____

What type of equipment do you provide? _____

_____

_____

What equipment would you need? _____

_____

_____

Do you need any electrical outlets? _____

What are your space requirements? _____

_____

How much time do you need to set up? _____

Do you provide any special effects, lighting? _____

What do you normally wear at weddings? _____

Would you be willing to wear specified attire? _____

Can you act as Master of Ceremonies? _____

How many breaks do you take? _____

How long are the breaks? _____

Do you provide background music during your breaks? _____

Prices

Hourly rate _____

Flat fee _____

Gratuity and taxes _____

Overtime rate _____

Comments_____

_____

Please make duplicate copies if necessary

Reception Music Selections

Activity	Time/Cue	Selection
Receiving line	_____	_____
	_____	_____
Newlyweds' arrival	_____	_____
Background music	_____	_____
	_____	_____
	_____	_____
	_____	_____
	_____	_____
	_____	_____
First dance	_____	_____
Special requests	_____	_____
	_____	_____
	_____	_____
	_____	_____
	_____	_____
	_____	_____
	_____	_____
Cake cutting ceremony	_____	_____
Bouquet toss	_____	_____
Garter removal	_____	_____
Garter toss	_____	_____
Last dance	_____	_____

Photography and Videography

$\mathcal{Y}$our wedding photographs will visually and emotionally capture your wedding story, letting you relive the beauty, excitement and the special moments for years to come.

Wedding Photography Tips

As soon as the wedding date is set, and the ceremony and reception sites are reserved, start interviewing photographers. Ask friends and family members for referrals. Also, ask wedding professionals for their recommendations. Use the *Wedding Vendors Referral Form* (pages 63-64) to keep track of and follow up with referrals. Bridal shows are a good place to meet professional photographers and see samples of their work. Collect their brochures and business cards and keep them in the pockets provided in this wedding planner.

Select and reserve your photographer six to twelve months before the wedding. Use the *Selecting a Photographer* (page 220) form to help ensure the best hiring decision.

Ask for at least three references from potential photographers and follow up with each one.

Ask potential photographers to view sample photo albums of the person who would be photographing your wedding.

Ask the ceremony and reception sites about restrictions regarding photography.

Hire someone who specializes in wedding photography and, preferably, someone

who is familiar with your ceremony and reception sites. Some photographers can also provide videography services.

Most photographers offer special wedding packages to suit every budget.

Features to look for include:

1. Number of hours included
2. Number of photographs taken
3. Number of prints and sizes included in package
4. Camera format
5. Bride and groom album
6. Parent albums
7. Wall portraits
8. Engagement portraits
9. Gift folios
10. Additional prints and albums
11. Reorder prices
12. Special effects
13. Retouch artwork
14. Black and white glossy for the newspaper announcement

Once you have selected a photographer for your wedding, get everything in writing and sign a contract! Pay the smallest deposit you can and pay with a credit card. Use the *Photography Worksheet* (pages 221-22) as a letter of agreement. This worksheet describes the products and services your photographer provides.

Go over the *Photo and Video Checklist* (pages 229-30) with your photographer one month before the wedding. Give them a copy of the checklist showing which photos you want them to take.

Delegate someone to be the "photographer's assistant," and give them a copy of the *Photo and Video Checklist*. This person should know who everyone is so they can help gather people needed for particular photo shots.

Decide if you want the posed photos taken before the ceremony. If you do, allow an hour and a half to two hours, and finish up one-half hour prior to the ceremony service. Let the wedding party know what time to arrive. Also, coordinate this with your florist so the flowers arrive in time for the photo session. You may also want to bring an extra set of candles so you can have them lit during the photo session and have new ones for the ceremony. If you are doing the posed photos after the ceremony, keep the photo session to a minimum length of time. Remember, your guests will already be at the reception site waiting for your arrival.

Discuss with your photographer whether photographs of your ceremony can be taken without flash from the back of the church. The attention should focus on you as you say your vows, not on the photographer.

Purchase special keepsake photo albums and photo frames to elegantly display your wedding photographs.

Photography Checklist

Due Date	To Do
❑ _____	Set a photography budget.
❑ _____	Reserve a photographer. (See: *Photography Worksheet*)
❑ _____	Sign agreements and pay deposits.
❑ _____	Schedule a sitting for the engagement portrait.
❑ _____	Schedule a sitting for the bridal portrait.
❑ _____	Decide which photos to have the photographer take. (See: *Photo and Video Checklist)*
❑ _____	Decide if the formal wedding pictures will be done before or after the ceremony, and inform bridal party members.
❑ _____	Recruit a volunteer to be the photographer's helper—someone who "knows everyone"—give them a copy of the *Photo and Video Checklist.*
❑ _____	Give photographer a copy of the *Photo and Video Checklist* (it lists which photos they should take at the ceremony and reception).
❑ _____	Confirm major photo details the month before your wedding.
❑ _____	Confirm *all* photo details two weeks before your wedding.
❑ _____	After the wedding: ❑ Schedule a time to view the proofs ❑ Find out when the finished photos will be ready to pickup ❑ Pay any balance owing
❑ _____	_____
❑ _____	_____
❑ _____	_____

Selecting a Photographer

Estimate

Appointment date_____ Time_____

Business _____

Address _____

_____

Contact_____ Phone_____

My budget for photography $ _____

Estimated total cost $ _____

Deposit required $ _____

Cancellation policy _____

References _____

_____

❑ Viewed sample album of photographer that
   would be shooting my wedding.

❑ Picked up price list and brochure.

Questions to Ask

Are you available at the date and time of my wedding?

_____

Will you be the one photographing my wedding? _____

Do you have an assistant who works with you?_____

Have you done a wedding at my ceremony site? _____
reception site? _____

How many years have you been photographing
weddings? _____

Do you specialize in weddings? _____

What associations are you a member of? _____

What do you normally wear when photographing
weddings? _____

Would you be willing to wear specified attire? _____

When would my proofs be ready? _____

How long will the prints take, once ordered? _____

How long do you keep the negatives?_____

Can I purchase the negatives? _____

Prices

Package prices (length of time, number of photographs, sizes and cost) _____

_____

_____

_____

_____

_____

How many hours does your price include? _____

Album rates_____

Individual picture prices _____

Bridal portrait _____

Engagement portrait _____

Portrait for newspaper announcements _____

Extra photo costs_____

Comments

_____

_____

_____

_____

Please make duplicate copies if necessary

Photography and Videography

Photography Worksheet

Studio _____

Address _____

Phone _____ Contact _____ ❑ Confirmed

Photographer _____ Phone _____

Photographer's assistant _____ Phone _____

Item	Sizes/ Description	Date Ordered	Pickup Date	Qty	Cost
Portraits					
❑ Engagement	___	___	___	___	___
❑ Bridal	___	___	___	___	___
❑ Other	___	___	___	___	___
Albums					
❑ Bride/groom	___	___	___	___	___
❑ Parents	___	___	___	___	___
❑ Parents	___	___	___	___	___
❑ Other	___	___	___	___	___
Prints / Reprints					
❑ 16 x 20	___	___	___	___	___
❑ 11 x 14	___	___	___	___	___
❑ 8 x 10	___	___	___	___	___
❑ 5 x 7	___	___	___	___	___
❑ 4 x 5	___	___	___	___	___
❑ 3 x 5	___	___	___	___	___
❑ Wallet	___	___	___	___	___
❑ Proofs	___	___	___	___	___
❑ Negatives	___	___	___	___	___

Photography Package Description

_____

_____

Photography Worksheet ———————————————

Service	Date	Time	Location
❑ Engagement portrait sitting	_____	____ to ____	_____
❑ Bridal portrait sitting	_____	____ to ____	_____
❑ Rehearsal photography	_____	____ to ____	_____
❑ Ceremony photography	_____	____ to ____	_____
❑ Reception photography	_____	____ to ____	_____

Is photographer familiar with the ceremony and reception sites? _____

Ceremony site photography restrictions _____

Reception site photography restrictions_____

Number of photographers and assistants_____

Photographer's attire _____

Type of equipment to be used _____

Special effects / lighting _____

Date proofs will be ready _____

Who keeps the negatives _____

How many years does the photographer keep negatives _____

Number of proofs _____

Number of hours price includes _____

Number of locations price includes _____

Date and time to review the proofs _____

COST

Budget _____ Actual _____

Paid by: ❑ Credit Card ❑ Check ❑ Cash

Photographer's fee _____ Package rate_____

Portraits _____ Wedding albums _____

Prints _____

Travel fee _____ Overtime rate _____

Deposit _____ Date due _____ ❑ Deposit paid

Balance _____ Date due_____ ❑ Balance paid

Cancellation policy _____

_____   _____
Service Representative Signature   Date

_____   _____
Bridal Party Signature   Date

Use this worksheet as an agreement form and have the service representative sign and date it.

Wedding Videography

Having a videotape of your wedding will keep the magic of your special day alive and it will become one your most treasured possessions. A good videographer will capture all the beauty and emotion of the ceremony as well as the fun and excitement of the reception. Videotaping your wedding is also a great way to share your wedding with friends and relatives who could not attend the wedding.

WEDDING VIDEOGRAPHY TIPS

As soon as the wedding date is set, and the ceremony and reception sites are reserved, start interviewing videographers. Ask friends and family members for referrals. Also, ask wedding professionals for their recommendations. Use the *Wedding Vendors Referral Form* (pages 63-64) to keep track of and follow up with referrals. Bridal shows are a good place to meet professional videographers and see samples of their work. Collect their brochures and business cards and keep them in the pockets provided in this wedding planner.

Ask the ceremony and reception sites about restrictions regarding videotaping before you hire a videographer.

Select and reserve a videographer six to twelve months before the wedding. Use the *Selecting a Videographer* (page 226) form to ensure the best hiring decision.

Ask for at least three references from potential videographers and follow up with each one.

Ask potential videographers to view sample videotapes of the person who would be filming your wedding. Watch for sound, style, quality, lighting, color, brightness, smoothness of the picture and any special effects.

Hire someone who specializes in wedding videography and, preferably, someone who is familiar with your ceremony and reception sites.

Most videographers offer special wedding packages to suit every budget. Features to look for include:

1. Number of cameras used
2. Number of hours included
3. Attendance at rehearsal
4. Opening title
5. Pre-wedding interview

6. Pre-ceremony coverage

7. Wireless microphones

8. Personalized titles listing your wedding party

9. Music sound track

10. Photo montage

11. Special effects: slow motion, multi-screen, audio dub, titling

12. Editing, is it included or is there an extra charge

13. Write your own personal "thank-you" credits

14. The number of VHS copies you will receive

15. Wedding only, reception only, or complete coverage of wedding and reception

16. Length of finished tape

Once you have selected a videographer for your wedding, get everything in writing and sign a contract! Pay the smallest deposit you can and pay with a credit card. Use the *Videography Worksheet* (pages 227-28) as a letter of agreement. This worksheet describes the products and services your videographer provides.

Go over the *Photo and Video Checklist* (pages 229-30) with your videographer one month before the wedding. Give them a copy of the checklist showing which events you want filmed.

Delegate someone to be the "videographer's assistant," and give them a copy of the *Photo and Video Checklist*. This person should know who everyone is so they can help the videographer film the requested events.

Purchase a special keepsake video box to elegantly keep and display your wedding video.

Videography Checklist

Due Date	To Do

❑ _____ Set a videography budget.

❑ _____ Reserve a videographer. (See: *Videography Worksheet*)

❑ _____ Decide which events to have videotaped. (See: *Photo and Video Checklist)*

❑ _____ Recruit a volunteer to be the videographer's helper—someone who "knows everyone," give them a copy of the *Photo and Video Checklist.*

❑ _____ Give videographer a copy of the *Photo and Video Checklist* (it lists which events they should film at the ceremony and reception).

❑ _____ Confirm major video details one month before your wedding.

❑ _____ Confirm all video details two weeks before your wedding.

❑ _____ After the wedding:
   ❑ Schedule a time to view the master tape
   ❑ Approve any special effects or editing to be done
   ❑ Find out when the finished tape(s) will be ready to pickup
   ❑ Pay any balance owing

❑ _____ _____

❑ _____ _____

❑ _____ _____

❑ _____ _____

❑ _____ _____

❑ _____ _____

❑ _____ _____

Selecting a Videographer ———————————————

Estimate

Appointment date _____ Time _____

Business _____

Address _____

_____

Contact _____ Phone _____

My budget for videography $ _____

Estimated total cost $ _____

Travel/other expenses _____

Deposit required $ _____

Cancellation policy _____

References _____

_____

❏ Viewed sample videotapes of videographer
 that would be filming my wedding.

❏ Picked up price list and brochure.

Questions to Ask

Are you available at the date and time of my
wedding? _____

Will you be the one videotaping my wedding? __

Do you have an assistant who works with you? ___

Have you done a wedding at my ceremony site?
reception site?_____

How many years have you been videotaping
weddings? _____

Do you specialize in weddings? _____

What associations are you a member of? _____

What do you normally wear when videotaping
weddings? _____

Would you be willing to wear specified attire? __

Do you require any special lighting? _____

_____

Do you need any electrical outlets? _____

What type of equipment do you use? _____

_____

How many cameras do you use?_____

Do you use a wireless microphone? _____

What type of editing do you do?
 ❏ in camera ❏ post edited

Prices

Package prices_____

_____

_____

_____

_____

_____

Videographer's fee_____

How many hours does your price include? ____

Editing fee _____

Fee to add still photos_____

Fee to add music_____

Fee to add opening title_____

Fee for copies _____

Comments

_____

_____

_____

_____

Please make duplicate copies if necessary

Photography and Videography

Videography Worksheet ——————————————

Company _____
Address _____
Phone _____ Contact _____ ☐ Confirmed
Videographer _____ Phone _____
Videographer's assistant _____ Phone _____
Date and time to view master tape _____
Date video tape(s) available for pick-up _____

Videography package description

_____
_____

Service	Date	Time arrive/depart	Location
☐ Rehearsal videography	_____	_____	_____
☐ Pre-ceremony videography	_____	_____	_____
☐ Ceremony videography	_____	_____	_____
☐ Reception videography	_____	_____	_____

References_____ ☐ Checked
References_____ ☐ Checked
Is videographer familiar with the ceremony and reception sites _____
Ceremony site videography restrictions _____
Reception site videography restrictions _____
Number of videographers and assistants _____
Videographer's attire _____
Quality of recording tapes to be used _____
Type of equipment to be used_____
Number of cameras to be used _____
Special effects _____
Add still photos to tape _____
Add music to tape _____
Add opening title to tape _____
Special lighting needs _____
Electrical outlet needs _____

Photography and Videography

Number of hours price includes _____

Number of locations price includes _____

Number and length of tapes price includes _____

COST

Budget_____ Actual _____

Paid by: ❑ Credit Card ❑ Check ❑ Cash

Videographer's fee _____ Package rate _____

Hourly Rate_____ Travel fee _____

Prints _____

Overtime rate _____ Other _____

Deposit_____ Date due _____ ❑ Deposit paid

Balance_____ Date due _____ ❑ Balance paid

Cancellation policy _____

_____
Service Representative Signature

_____
Date

_____
Bridal Party Signature

_____
Date

Use this worksheet as an agreement form and have the service representative sign and date it.

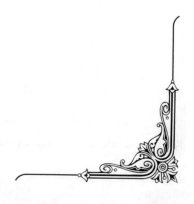

Photo and Video Checklist

Put a check mark in front of the photos and/or videos you want your photographer and videographer to take. Give copies of this list to your photographer and videographer and their assistants. Have them check off which shots they actually took.

(P)hotography or (V)ideo

Before the Ceremony

(P) (V)
- ❏ ❏ Bride getting ready
- ❏ ❏ Mother adjusting bride's veil
- ❏ ❏ Bride in dress
- ❏ ❏ Bride looking in mirror
- ❏ ❏ Bridesmaids in dressing room
- ❏ ❏ Putting on the garter
- ❏ ❏ Putting the penny in the shoe
- ❏ ❏ Bride with mother
- ❏ ❏ Bride with father
- ❏ ❏ Bride with both parents
- ❏ ❏ Bride with siblings
- ❏ ❏ Bride with honor attendant(s)
- ❏ ❏ Bride with bridesmaids
- ❏ ❏ Bride leaving for ceremony
- ❏ ❏ Bride & father getting into car
- ❏ ❏ Groom getting ready
- ❏ ❏ Groom alone
- ❏ ❏ Groom with mother
- ❏ ❏ Groom with father
- ❏ ❏ Groom with both parents
- ❏ ❏ Groom with siblings
- ❏ ❏ Groom with best man
- ❏ ❏ Groom with ushers
- ❏ ❏ Men putting on boutonnieres
- ❏ ❏ Groom leaving for ceremony
- ❏ ❏ The wedding party

The Ceremony

(P) (V)
- ❏ ❏ View of ceremony site
- ❏ ❏ The altar
- ❏ ❏ Decorations
- ❏ ❏ Bride and father arriving
- ❏ ❏ Guests arriving
- ❏ ❏ Guests signing in guest book
- ❏ ❏ Ushers escorting guests
- ❏ ❏ Groom's parents being seated
- ❏ ❏ Brides' mother being seated
- ❏ ❏ Groom and ushers at altar
- ❏ ❏ Bridesmaids procession
- ❏ ❏ Bride's procession
- ❏ ❏ Groom's expression
- ❏ ❏ Father giving away bride
- ❏ ❏ Groom meeting bride
- ❏ ❏ Exchanging vows
- ❏ ❏ Lighting the unity candle
- ❏ ❏ Ring exchange
- ❏ ❏ The kiss
- ❏ ❏ Recessional
- ❏ ❏ Receiving line
- ❏ ❏ Signing marriage license
- ❏ ❏ Bride & groom getting into car
- ❏ ❏ Bride & groom in back seat

Photo and Video Checklist ——————————

(P)hotography or (V)ideo

Posted Shots

(P) (V)

- ❏ ❏ Shots taken before ceremony
- ❏ ❏ Shots taken after ceremony
- ❏ ❏ Bride alone
- ❏ ❏ Groom alone
- ❏ ❏ Bride and groom together
- ❏ ❏ Bride with honor attendant(s)
- ❏ ❏ Bride with all bridesmaids
- ❏ ❏ Bride with each bridesmaid
- ❏ ❏ Bride with ushers
- ❏ ❏ Bride with her parents
- ❏ ❏ Bride with grandparents
- ❏ ❏ Groom with best man
- ❏ ❏ Groom with all ushers
- ❏ ❏ Groom with each usher
- ❏ ❏ Groom with bridesmaids
- ❏ ❏ Groom with his parents
- ❏ ❏ Groom with grandparents
- ❏ ❏ Bride, groom wedding party
- ❏ ❏ Bride, groom with her family
- ❏ ❏ Bride, groom with his family
- ❏ ❏ Bride, groom with all parents
- ❏ ❏ Bride, groom with grandparents
- ❏ ❏ Bride, groom with children
- ❏ ❏ Bride, groom with officiant
- ❏ ❏ Bride, groom's hands with rings
- ❏ ❏ Both families together

At the Reception

(P) (V)

- ❏ ❏ Bride and groom's arrival
- ❏ ❏ Receiving line
- ❏ ❏ Bride, groom's grand entrance
- ❏ ❏ Guests signing the guest book
- ❏ ❏ Bride's table
- ❏ ❏ Parents' table(s)
- ❏ ❏ Guests' tables
- ❏ ❏ Buffet tables
- ❏ ❏ Cake table
- ❏ ❏ Gift table
- ❏ ❏ Bride and groom's first dance
- ❏ ❏ Bride dancing with her father
- ❏ ❏ Bride dancing with father-in-law
- ❏ ❏ Groom dancing with his mother
- ❏ ❏ Groom dancing with mother-in-law
- ❏ ❏ Parents dancing
- ❏ ❏ Bridesmaids, ushers dancing
- ❏ ❏ Guests dancing
- ❏ ❏ Musicians
- ❏ ❏ Best man giving toast
- ❏ ❏ Cake cutting ceremony
- ❏ ❏ Feeding each other cake
- ❏ ❏ Bride and groom toasting
- ❏ ❏ Bride tossing bouquet
- ❏ ❏ Groom removing garter
- ❏ ❏ Groom tossing garter
- ❏ ❏ Decorated getaway car
- ❏ ❏ Guest throwing rice
- ❏ ❏ Bride, groom waving good-bye
- ❏ ❏ Back of car as it is leaving

Wedding Transportation

Wedding Transportation Tips

As soon as the wedding date is set, and the ceremony and reception sites are reserved, start interviewing transportation services. Ask friends and family members for referrals. Also, ask wedding professionals for their recommendations. Use the *Wedding Vendors Referral Form* (pages 63-64) to keep track of and follow up with referrals. Bridal shows are a good place to meet with limousine services, as they usually have some of their stretch limos parked out front. Collect their brochures and business cards and keep them in the pockets provided in this wedding planner.

Select and reserve your transportation six to twelve months before the wedding. Use the *Selecting Wedding Day Transportation* (pages 234-35) form to ensure the best hiring decision.

Ask for at least three references from potential transportation services, and follow up with each one.

Ask potential services to view the actual limousine(s) or car(s) you would use for transportation. Also, ask about insurance and permits. All limousines are required to carry commercial insurance and proper permits.

Determine how many people need transportation and what type of transportation is desired. The wedding party and out-of-town guests may arrive in private or rented vehicles, but you, the bride, may want a limousine. For something more dramatic you might consider the following:

Wedding Transportation

- Vintage car (Cadillac, Rolls Royce)
- Sports or luxury car (Porsche, Corvette, Mercedes Benz, Ferrari)
- Horse-drawn carriage
- Horseback
- Hot-air balloon
- Horse-drawn sleigh

Full service transportation companies offer special wedding packages to suit every budget. Features to look for include:

1. Minimum number of hours required

2. Complimentary champagne and other beverages

3. Full wet bar

4. Decorations and balloons

5. Flowers

6. Red carpet

7. Color TV-VCR

8. Privacy divider

9. Cellular phones

10. Moon roof

11. Halo lighting

Once you have selected a transportation company for your wedding, get everything in writing and sign a contract! Pay the smallest deposit you can and pay with a credit card. Use the *Transportation Worksheet* (page 236) as a letter of agreement. This worksheet describes the products and services your transportation company provides.

Complete the *Wedding Day Transportation Schedule* (page 237) and give a copy to all the drivers. They need to know where people must be picked up and when they must be at each location.

Make sure all the drivers know the ceremony and reception site locations and how to get there.

Transporation Checklist ———————————————

Due Date	To Do

❑ _____ Determine how many people need transportation. The bride and groom can provide transportation for the wedding party; however, the attendants are usually responsible for their own transportation to and from the wedding and reception.

❑ _____ Determine if you will need transportation:
   ❑ To the ceremony site:
      ____ Bride ____Groom ____ Attendants ____ Parents

   ❑ To the reception site:
      ____ Bride ____Groom ____ Attendants ____ Parents

   ❑ From the reception site:
      ____ Bride ____Groom ____ Attendants ____ Parents

   ❑ Decide what mode of transportation you want for:
      ❑ Bride and groom _____
      ❑ Attendants' parents _____
      ❑ Grandparents _____
      ❑ Out-of-town guests _____

❑ _____ Visit transportation services and inspect vehicles, check references. (See: *Selecting Wedding Transportation*)

❑ _____ Reserve transportation, six to twelve months before the wedding. (See: *Transportation Worksheet*)

❑ _____ Sign agreements and pay deposits.

❑ _____ Fill out the *Wedding Day Transportation Schedule*, and give copies to all the drivers.

❑ _____ Confirm major transportation details one month before your wedding.

❑ _____ Confirm all transportation details two weeks before your wedding.

Selecting Wedding Transportation ———————————

Appointment date _____ Time _____

Business _____

Address_____

Contact_____ Phone _____

My budget for transportation $ _____

Estimated total cost _____

Travel/other expenses _____

Deposit required _____ Cancellation policy _____

References _____

_____

_____

❑ Viewed vehicles we would be renting.
❑ Picked up price list and brochure.

Questions to Ask

What dates are available?_____

What times are available? _____

What is the minimum rental time?_____

What is your policy on decorating the vehicle? _____

What is the chauffeur's attire? _____

How many years have you been in business? _____

Do you specialize in weddings? _____

What insurance and permits do you have? _____

Mode of Transportation

❑ Limousine   ❑ Vintage car   ❑ Horse-drawn carriage
❑ Sleigh   ❑ Luxury rental car
❑ Other _____

Please make duplicate copies if necessary

Selecting Wedding Transporation ————————

Vehicle Description

Number of passengers _____

Vehicle colors _____

- ❑ Full wet bar
- ❑ Moon roof
- ❑ Privacy divider
- ❑ Other _____
- ❑ Cellular phone
- ❑ Color television
- ❑ Intercom
- ❑ Halo lighting
- ❑ VCR

Prices

Hourly rates _____

Special rates _____

_____

_____

_____

Is the fee based on rental time? _____

Is the fee based on distance? _____

Gratuity and taxes _____

Overtime rate _____

Comments

_____

_____

_____

_____

_____

_____

_____

_____

Please make duplicate copies if necessary

Wedding Transportation

Transportation Worksheet _____

Business _____

Address _____

Phone _____ Contact _____ ❑ Confirmed

Service Information

Date of service _____ Time of service _____

Ceremony arrival time _____ Location _____

Reception arrival time _____ Location _____

❑ Vehicle inspection completed   ❑ Proof of insurance _____

Vehicle / Service description _____

_____

_____

Transportation Services

_____   _____ @ $_____ = $_____
Vehicle Type/Service   Total hours   Hourly rate   Total cost

_____   _____ @ $_____ = $_____
Vehicle Type/Service   Total hours   Hourly rate   Total cost

Cost

Budget _____ Actual _____

Paid by: ❑ Credit Card   ❑ Check   ❑ Cash

Other charges _____

Deposit _____ Date due _____ ❑ Deposit paid

Balance _____ Date due _____ ❑ Balance paid

Cancellation policy _____

_____   _____

Service Representative Signature   Date

_____   _____

Bridal Party Signature   Date

Use this worksheet as an agreement form and have the service representatives sign and date it.

Wedding Day Transportation Schedule ———————

TRANSPORTATION TO CEREMONY SITE

Ceremony address _____

Pickup Time	Name	Pickup Location	Vehicle
_____	_____	_____	_____
_____	_____	_____	_____
_____	_____	_____	_____
_____	_____	_____	_____
_____	_____	_____	_____

TRANSPORTATION TO RECEPTION SITE

Reception site address _____

Pickup Time	Name	Vehicle
_____	_____	_____
_____	_____	_____
_____	_____	_____
_____	_____	_____
_____	_____	_____

TRANSPORTATION FROM RECEPTION SITE

Pickup Time	Name	Destination	Vehicle
_____	_____	_____	_____
_____	_____	_____	_____
_____	_____	_____	_____
_____	_____	_____	_____
_____	_____	_____	_____

Fill in this form and give copies to all the drivers.

Notes

_____

_____

_____

_____

_____

_____

_____

_____

_____

_____

_____

_____

_____

_____

_____

_____

_____

_____

_____

_____

_____

_____

The
Honeymoon

Honeymoon Planning Tips

As soon as the wedding date and honeymoon budget are set, begin planning the honeymoon. Ask friends and family members for referrals of travel agents. Also, ask wedding professionals for their recommendations. Use the *Wedding Vendors Referral Form* (pages 63-64) to keep track of and follow up with referrals. Bridal shows are a good place to meet travel agents that specialize in honeymoons. Collect their brochures and business cards and keep them in the pockets provided in this wedding planner.

Look through bridal magazines for ideas and information on honeymoon locations.

Select a reliable travel agent to help you with your honeymoon plans. They can provide you with information on popular honeymoon destinations and advice about accommodations, transportation and entertainment.

There are a variety of options to consider when you are trying to determine your honeymoon destination and itinerary. To help you plan your ideal honeymoon, consider the following:

Season: ❑ Winter ❑ Spring ❑ Summer ❑ Fall

Theme: ❑ Historical sight-seeing ❑ Outdoor adventure
❑ Exotic ❑ Tropical ❑ Active ❑ Relaxing
❑ Entertaining ❑ Romantic

The Honeymoon

Locations: ❏ U.S. ❏ Canada ❏ Mexico
❏ International

Travel/Transportation:
❏ Fly ❏ Drive ❏ Train
❏ Bus ❏ Cruise ship

Accommodations:
❏ Hotel ❏ Resort ❏ All-inclusive resort
❏ Condominium ❏ Bed & breakfast
❏ Camping ❏ Cabin ❏ Cruise ship

Activities:

❏ Downhill skiing ❏ Swimming
❏ Cross-country skiing ❏ Tennis
❏ Sledding ❏ Golf/Miniature golf
❏ Snowmobiling ❏ Fishing
❏ Ice skating ❏ Horseback riding
❏ Horse-drawn sleigh ride ❏ White water rafting
❏ Museums ❏ Water skiing
❏ Theater ❏ Hiking
❏ Ballet ❏ Mountain climbing
❏ Wine tasting ❏ Fitness center
❏ Historical sites ❏ Entertainment parks
❏ Dancing ❏ Fine dining

Once you have determined your honeymoon destination, have everything confirmed in writing. Pay the smallest deposit you can and pay with a credit card. Use the *Honeymoon Worksheet* (page 243-45) as a letter of confirmation. This worksheet describes your itinerary, transportation schedules, lodging reservations and other services your travel agent has booked for you.

Complete the *Honeymoon Document Checklist* (page 246) and the *Honeymoon Packing Checklist* (page 247) and begin packing for your honeymoon one month before your wedding.

The Honeymoon

Honeymoon Checklist

Due Date	To Do

☐ _____ Set a honeymoon budget.

☐ _____ Make reservations for your first night together:
    ☐ Reserve special accommodations
    ☐ Make dinner reservations
    ☐ Make brunch reservations
    ☐ Reserve special transportation

☐ _____ Select a travel agent.

☐ _____ Determine honeymoon destination and make reservations for:
    ☐ Travel
    ☐ Accommodations
    ☐ Transportation

☐ _____ Sign agreements and pay deposits.

☐ _____ Make arrangements for time-off from work.

☐ _____ Arrange for passports and visas.

☐ _____ Gather important documents together. (See: *Honeymoon Document Checklist*)

☐ _____ Shop for honeymoon wardrobe and new luggage.

☐ _____ Obtain traveler's checks and exchange money.

☐ _____ Pick up travel tickets and written confirmation of travel plans.

☐ _____ Pack suitcases for wedding night and honeymoon. (See: *Honeymoon Packing Checklist*)

☐ _____ Record credit card information and checking account numbers (in case they are lost or stolen). (See: *Honeymoon Document Checklist*)

☐ _____ Take important names and numbers (in case of an emergency). (See: *Honeymoon Document Checklist*)

☐ _____ Leave travel plan information with family members.

☐ _____ Make arrangements to have someone pick up the mail, water plants, feed animals, watch house, stop newspaper service, etc.

☐ _____ Confirm all details of your honeymoon two weeks before your wedding.

The Honeymoon

Selecting a Wedding Night Hotel ——————————

Appointment date _____ Time _____

Business _____

Address_____

Contact _____ Phone _____

My budget for the wedding night $_____

Estimated total cost_____

Deposit required_____ Cancellation policy _____

❏ Viewed rooms available.

❏ Picked up price list and brochure.

Questions to Ask

Is my date available? _____

What time can we check in?_____

What time do we have to check out?_____

What room features and amenities do you provide?

❏ View   ❏ Room service   ❏ Breakfast in bed   ❏ Fireplace in the room

❏ Hot tub in the room   ❏ Wet bar in the room   ❏ Swimming pool

❏ Exercise room   ❏ Restaurant on-site, type: _____

❏ Newlywed gift basket   ❏ Complimentary champagne   ❏ Flowers

Other _____

Prices

Daily room rate _____ Taxes _____

Health club _____ Parking fee/valet service _____

Comments

_____

_____

_____

Please make duplicate copies if necessary

The Honeymoon

Honeymoon Worksheet _____

Travel Agency _____

Address _____

Phone Contact _____ ❏ Confirmed_____

Destination _____

Travel dates: from _____ to _____

Tickets will be delivered on _____ ❏ will be picked up by _____
\hspace{9em} Date \hspace{16em} Date

Itinerary

Departure _____

_____

Arrival _____

_____

Return _____

_____

Flight Schedule

Date _____ Leave _____ Arrive _____
\hspace{15em} (City and Time) \hspace{9em} (City and Time)

Seat assignments _____ Carrier/Flight # _____
Confirmation # _____

Date _____ Leave _____ Arrive _____
\hspace{15em} (City and Time) \hspace{9em} (City and Time)

Seat assignments _____ Carrier/Flight # _____
Confirmation # _____

Date _____ Leave _____ Arrive _____
\hspace{15em} (City and Time) \hspace{9em} (City and Time)

Seat assignments _____ Carrier/Flight # _____
Confirmation # _____

The Honeymoon

Honeymoon Worksheet ——————————————————

Airline Travel Cost

Budget _____ Actual _____

Paid by: ❑ Credit Card ❑ Check ❑ Cash

Deposit _____ Date due _____ ❑ Deposit paid

Balance _____ Date due _____ ❑ Balance paid

Cancellation policy _____

Car Rental Agency _____

Address _____

Phone _____ Contact _____ ❑ Confirmed

Confirmation # _____

Vehicle description _____

Pickup date/time _____ Return date/time _____

Daily rate _____ Number of days _____

Budget _____ Actual _____

Paid by: ❑ Credit Card ❑ Check ❑ Cash

Deposit _____ Date due _____ ❑ Deposit paid

Balance _____ Date due _____ ❑ Balance paid

Cancellation policy _____

Hotel/Lodging _____

Address _____

Phone _____ Contact _____ ❑ Confirmed

Confirmation # _____

Arrival date_____ Departure date _____

Daily rate _____ Number of days _____

Budget _____ Actual _____

Paid by: ❑ Credit Card ❑ Check ❑ Cash

Honeymoon Worksheet ───────────────

Deposit _____ Date due _____ ❑ Deposit paid

Balance _____ Date due _____ ❑ Balance paid

Cancellation policy _____

Description of room/amenities _____

_____

_____

Daily rate_____ Number of days_____

Budget _____ Actual_____

Paid by: ❑ Credit Card   ❑ Check   ❑ Cash

Deposit _____ Date due _____ ❑ Deposit paid

Balance _____ Date due _____ ❑ Balance paid

Cancellation policy _____

Notes

_____

_____

_____

_____

_____

_____

_____

_____

_____

_____

_____

_____

The Honeymoon

Honeymoon Document Checklist ————————————

DOCUMENTS

Bride	Groom	Item	Account Number (if applicable)
❏	❏	Airline tickets	_____
❏	❏	Copy of birth certificate	_____
❏	❏	Copies of prescriptions	_____
❏	❏	Driver's license	_____
❏	❏	Marriage license	_____
❏	❏	Medical insurance card	_____
❏	❏	Passports	_____
❏	❏	Visas	_____

CREDIT CARDS

Bride	Groom	Type of Card	Account Number
❏	❏	_____	_____
❏	❏	_____	_____
❏	❏	_____	_____
❏	❏	_____	_____

CHECKING ACCOUNT NUMBERS

Bride	Groom	Bank	Account Number
❏	❏	_____	_____
❏	❏	_____	_____

TRAVELER'S CHECKS

Bank _____

Address _____ Phone _____

Traveler's check numbers _____

_____

MEDICAL INFORMATION

Bride's doctor _____

Medical conditions _____

Groom's doctor _____

Medical conditions _____

Honeymoon Packing Checklist

PERSONAL ITEMS

Need to Purchase	Packed	Item
❑	❑	Aspirin
❑	❑	Birth control
❑	❑	Brush/comb
❑	❑	Contact lenses
❑	❑	Cosmetics
❑	❑	Cotton balls
❑	❑	Curling iron
❑	❑	Dental floss
❑	❑	Deodorant
❑	❑	Eyeglasses
❑	❑	First-aid kit
❑	❑	Hair clips/pins
❑	❑	Hair conditioner
❑	❑	Hair shampoo
❑	❑	Hairdryer
❑	❑	Hair rollers
❑	❑	Hairspray
❑	❑	Insect repellant
❑	❑	Lotion
❑	❑	Manicure kit
❑	❑	Medications
❑	❑	Mouthwash
❑	❑	Perfume/cologne
❑	❑	Q-tips
❑	❑	Razor & blades
❑	❑	Shower cap
❑	❑	Soap
❑	❑	Sunglasses
❑	❑	Sunscreen
❑	❑	Tampon/pads
❑	❑	Toothbrush
❑	❑	Toothpaste

EQUIPMENT

Need to Purchase	Packed	Item
❑	❑	Address book
❑	❑	Alarm clock
❑	❑	Batteries
❑	❑	Calculator
❑	❑	Camera
❑	❑	Camera film
❑	❑	Camera lenses
❑	❑	Cassette player
❑	❑	Cassettes
❑	❑	Current adapter
❑	❑	Dictionary
❑	❑	Flashlight
❑	❑	Guide books
❑	❑	Maps
❑	❑	Memo pads
❑	❑	Pens
❑	❑	Pencils
❑	❑	Radio
❑	❑	Sewing kit
❑	❑	Scissors
❑	❑	Travel iron
❑	❑	Video recorder
❑	❑	Videotapes

MISCELLANEOUS

Need to Purchase	Packed	Item
❑	❑	_____
❑	❑	_____
❑	❑	_____
❑	❑	_____
❑	❑	_____
❑	❑	_____
❑	❑	_____

Honeymoon Itinerary

Monday	Tuesday

Wednesday	Thursday

Friday	Saturday/Sunday

After the Wedding

After the Wedding Checklist

Due Date　　　　　　　　　　　**To Do**

❑ _____ Wedding announcements sent. Announcements are sent to those not invited to the wedding. They should be mailed out on the wedding day or just after the wedding.

❑ _____ Thank-you cards sent. These should be sent out within a month after the wedding.

❑ _____ Wedding gown cleaned and preserved.

❑ _____ Wedding bouquet preserved.

❑ _____ Groom's formal wear returned.

❑ _____ Top layer of wedding cake preserved for first anniversary.

❑ _____ Wedding cake stands and pillars returned to bakery.

❑ _____ Wedding albums picked up from photographer.

❑ _____ Distribute pictures and albums to family and friends.

❑ _____ Wedding video received from videographer.

❑ _____ Name and address changed on important documents. See: *Name and Address Change Checklist* (page 251).

❑ _____ Change of address cards sent.

❑ _____ Rental items returned.

❑ _____ Exchange duplicate or unusable wedding gifts.

❑ _____ _____

❑ _____ _____

❑ _____ _____

❑ _____ _____

❑ _____ _____

❑ _____ _____

❑ _____ _____

After The Wedding

Name and Address Change Checklist

Notes

- ❏ Auto insurance
- ❏ Auto registration
- ❏ Bank accounts
- ❏ Business cards
- ❏ Business stationery
- ❏ Credit cards
- ❏ Dental insurance
- ❏ Dental records
- ❏ Driver's license
- ❏ Employment records
- ❏ Homeowner's insurance
- ❏ IRA accounts
- ❏ Investments
- ❏ Leases
- ❏ Life insurance
- ❏ Loans
- ❏ Magazines
- ❏ Medical insurance
- ❏ Medical records
- ❏ Memberships
- ❏ Newspapers
- ❏ Passports / Visas
- ❏ Pensions
- ❏ Post Office
- ❏ Property insurance
- ❏ Property titles
- ❏ Renter's insurance
- ❏ Safety deposit box
- ❏ School records
- ❏ Social security card
- ❏ Taxes
- ❏ Telephone company
- ❏ Utilities
- ❏ Voter registration
- ❏ Wills/Trusts

About the Author

*C*athy J. Bouchard is the owner and designer of America's largest wedding collection. An internationally renowned, award winning artist and designer for over twenty years, her work has been seen on over fifty television programs, commercials and movies, including Dynasty, L.A. Law, All My Children, General Hospital and One Life to Live. Reproductions of her art can be found in over half a million homes in forty-seven countries worldwide. Her extensive artistic background led her into custom designing gowns, jewelry and accessories for retail stores.

Today, her company, Bouchard Ltd., offers the bride and her wedding party the best selection in the industry—The Bouchard Wedding Collection, America's largest selection of fine bridal keepsakes, accessories and gift items.

For a store near you that carries the The Bouchard Wedding Collection Call 1-800-967-5467, or visit their website at www.BouchardLtd.com.

Acknowledgements

*S*pecial thanks to my friend, Di Ana Ford, for her invaluable help with the research and interviews needed for a planner this comprehensive.

And to my husband, Martin Lillig—thank you for your love and patience through yet another of your wife's projects.